Power Maths

Year 5 Practice Book 5C

D0413928

Draw three things that are in your bedroom. What 3D shapes can you find?

This book belongs to _____ .

My class is _____ .

Pearson

Contents

This looks like a good challenge!

Unit 14 – Geometry – properties of shapes (2)

Unit 15 – Geometry – position and direction

Unit 16 – Measure – converting units

Unit 17 – Measure – volume and capacity

It's time to do some practice!

How to use this book

How does this **Practice Book** work?

Use the **Textbook** first to learn how to solve this type of problem.

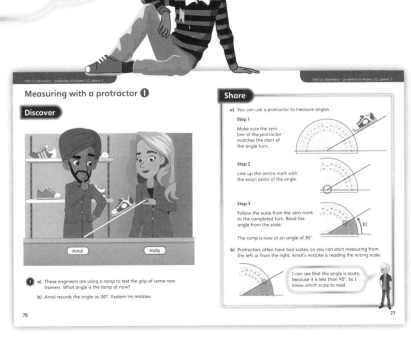

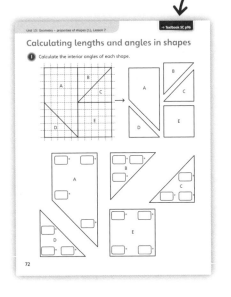

This shows you which **Textbook** page you need.

Have a go at questions by yourself using this **Practice Book**. Use what you have learnt.

Challenge questions make you think hard!

Questions with this light bulb make you think differently.

Reflect

Each lesson ends with a **Reflect** question so you can think about what you have learnt.

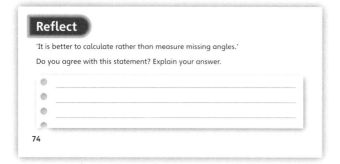

Reflect

'It is better to calculate rather than measure missing angles.'

Do you agree with this statement? Explain your answer.

74

Use **My power points** at the back of this book to keep track of what you have learnt.

My journal

At the end of a unit your teacher will ask you to fill in **My journal**.

This will help you show how much you can do now that you have finished the unit.

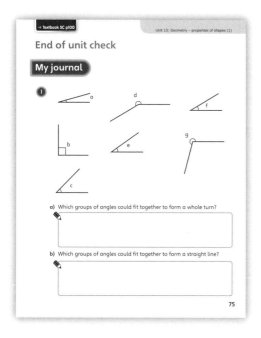

→ Textbook 5C p100

Unit 13: Geometry – properties of shapes (1)

End of unit check

My journal

1

a) Which groups of angles could fit together to form a whole turn?

b) Which groups of angles could fit together to form a straight line?

75

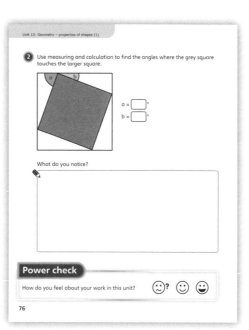

Unit 13: Geometry – properties of shapes (1)

2 Use measuring and calculation to find the angles where the grey square touches the larger square.

a = ☐ °
b = ☐ °

What do you notice?

Power check

How do you feel about your work in this unit?

76

5

Adding and subtracting decimals

1 Find the totals of these decimals.

a) 0·4 + 0·5 = [0.9]

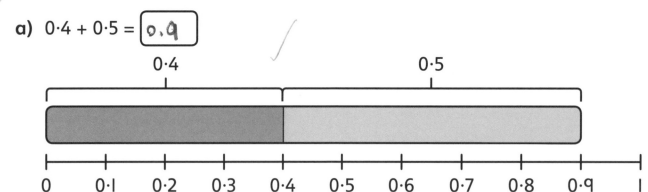

b) 0·7 + 0·1 + 0·1 = [0.9]

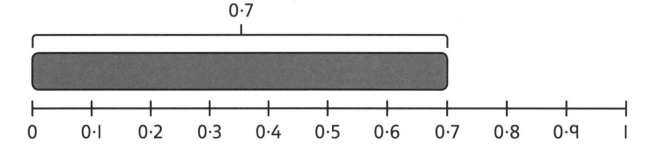

c) 0·3 + 0·1 + 0·3 = [0.7]   d) 0·5 + 0·5 = [1]

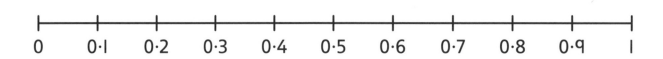

2 Max cuts some pieces of string. He measures the lengths.

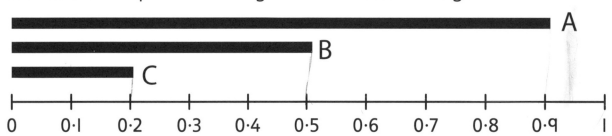

a) How much longer is A than B?   [0.5] − [0.9] = [0.4]

b) What is the difference between A and C?   [0.7] − [0.9] = [0.2]

3 Complete the part-whole models.

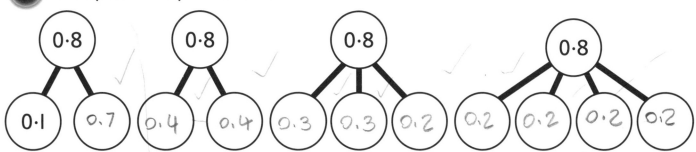

(0·8) — (0·1) (0,7)

(0·8) — (0,4) (0,4)

(0·8) — (0,3) (0,3) (0,2)

(0·8) — (0,2) (0,2) (0,2) (0,2)

4 Complete the calculations.

a) 0·3 + 0·5 = 0.8

b) 0·7 + 0·1 = 0.8

c) 0·2 + 0.3 = 0·5

d) 0·5 − 0·1 = 0,4

e) 0·8 − 0·2 = 0,6

f) 0·7 − 0.5 = 0·2

g) 0·4 + 0·3 + 0·2 = 0,9

h) 0·7 + 0·2 − 0·3 = 0,12

i) 0·9 − 0·1 + 0·2 = 1

j) 0·5 − 0·2 − 0·3 = 1

5 Complete the following calculations.

a) 0·3 + 0·7 = 1

b) 0·6 + 1·6 = 1

c) 1,1 + 0·1 = 1

d) 1 − 0·2 = 0,8

e) 1 − 0·5 = 0,5

f) 1 − 0,8 = 0·2

6 Complete the addition pyramids. Each row of the pyramid must total the same as the other rows.

a)

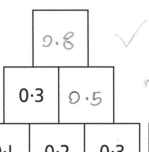

9,8

0·3 | 0,5

0·1 | 0·2 | 0·3

b)

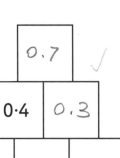

0,7

0·4 | 0,3

0,2 | 0·2 | 0·1

c)

0·8

0·5 | 0,3

0,4 | 0·1 | 0,2

d)

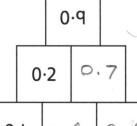

0·9

0·2 | 0,7

0·1 | 0,1 | 0,6

7 If ◆ and ▲ are two decimal numbers less than 1 and ▲ − ◆ = 0·3, what could ▲ and ◆ be?

▲ = ☐ ◆ = ☐ .

8 Write the numbers 0·1, 0·2, 0·3, 0·4, 0·5 and 0·6 in the circles so that the sum of each side of the triangle is equal to 0·9. Use each number once.

CHALLENGE

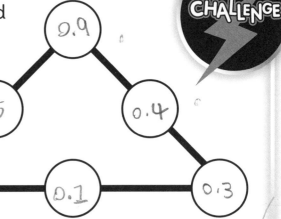

Reflect

Emma calculates 0·4 + 1 = 0·5. Explain the mistake Emma has made.

The mistake is that she thought 0·1 was 0·1 but it was really just 1 whole.

Adding and subtracting decimals ❷ 11.05.22

1 Mo adds different amounts of water and orange to make orange squash. Complete the additions.

Water 0·36 l

Orange 0·22 l

a) 0·36 l + 0·22 l = $\boxed{0.58}$ l ✓

O	•	Tth	Hth
	•	(0·1)(0·1)(0·1)	(0·01)(0·01)(0·01)(0·01)(0·01)
	•		(0·01)
	•	(0·1)(0·1)	(0·01)(0·01)

```
  O · Tth Hth
  0 ·  3   6
+ 0 ·  2   2
───────────
  0 ·  5   8
```
✓

b) 0·25 l + 0·47 l = $\boxed{0.72}$ l ✓

O	•	Tth	Hth
	•	(0·1)(0·1)	(0·01)(0·01)(0·01)(0·01)(0·01)
		(0·1)(0·1)(0·1)(0·1)	(0·01)(0·01)(0·01)(0·01)(0·01)
	•		(0·01)(0·01)

```
  O · Tth Hth
  0 ·  2¹   5
+ 0 ·  4   7
───────────
  0 ·  7   2
```

c) 0·55 + 0·31 = $\boxed{0.86}$ ✓

```
  O · Tth Hth
  0 ·  5   5
+ 0 ·  3   1
───────────
  0 ·  8   6
```

d) 0·38 + 0·38 = $\boxed{0.76}$ ✓

```
  O · Tth Hth
  0 ·  3¹  8
+ 0 ·  3   8
───────────
  0 ·  7   6
```

2 Kate works out 0·05 + 0·12 as a column addition. Explain Kate's mistake.

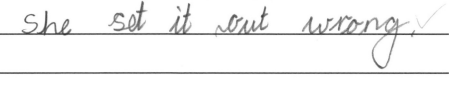

She set it out wrong. ✓

```
  O · Tth Hth
  0 ·  5  ̶5̶
+ 0 ·  1   2
───────────
  0 ·  6   2
```

9

3 A running race is 0·65 km long. Lee runs 0·34 km. How far is left to run?

0·65 km – 0·34 km = [0.31] km

O	•	Tth	Hth
	•	0·1 0·1 0·1 0·1 0·1	0·01 0·01 0·01 0·01 0·01
	•	0·1	

O	· Tth	Hth
0 ·	6	5
– 0 ·	3	4
0 ·	3	1

4 Complete the subtractions.

a) 0·92 – 0·58 = [0.34]

O	· Tth	Hth
0 ·	9̶8̶ 8̶	1̶2̶ 2
– 0 ·	5	8
0 ·	3	4

c) 0·71 – 0·24 = [0.47]

O	· Tth	Hth
0 ·	7̶6̶ 6	1̶1̶ 1
– 0 ·	2	4
0 ·	4	7

b) 0·49 - 0·19 = [0.30]

O	· Tth	Hth
0 ·	4	9
– 0 ·	1	9
0 ·	3	0

d) 0·60 – 0·45 = [0.15]

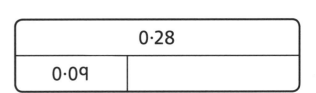

$$0.\overset{5}{\cancel{6}}\overset{}{1}0$$
$$-\,0.45$$
$$\overline{0.15}$$

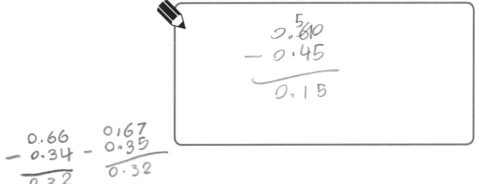

0.66
– 0.34
‾‾‾‾‾
0.32

0.67
– 0.35
‾‾‾‾‾
0.32

5 Complete the missing numbers in these models.

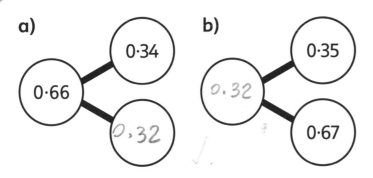

a)

0·66 — 0·34
0·66 — 0.32

b)

0.32 — 0·35
0.32 — 0·67

c)

	0·28
0·09	

10

6 Ambika is using a number line to work out a calculation.

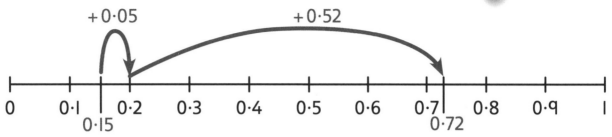

What two possible calculations might Ambika be working out?

_____

_____

7 Use four different digits from I, 2, 3, 4, 5, 6, 7, 8, 9 to:

a) Make the greatest total you can, less than I.

b) Make the greatest difference you can, less than I.

```
    0 · 2 3
  + 0 · 4 5
  _____
    0 · 6 8
```

```
    0 · 9 ̷1 6
  − 0 · 7 8
  _____
    0 · 2 8
```

Reflect

Explain how Alex can use 37 + 59 to find the sum of 0·37 and 0·59.

Alex can divide them by 100.

_____

_____

Adding and subtracting decimals ❸ 21.05.22

1 Use the hundredths grids to help you find the missing numbers.

a) 0·8 + [0.2] = 1

b) 0·69 + [31] = 1

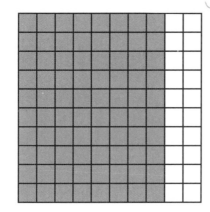
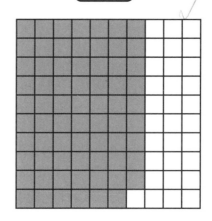

2 Draw lines to match the pairs that make 1 m when added together.

You may not be able to find a pair for all of the pieces.

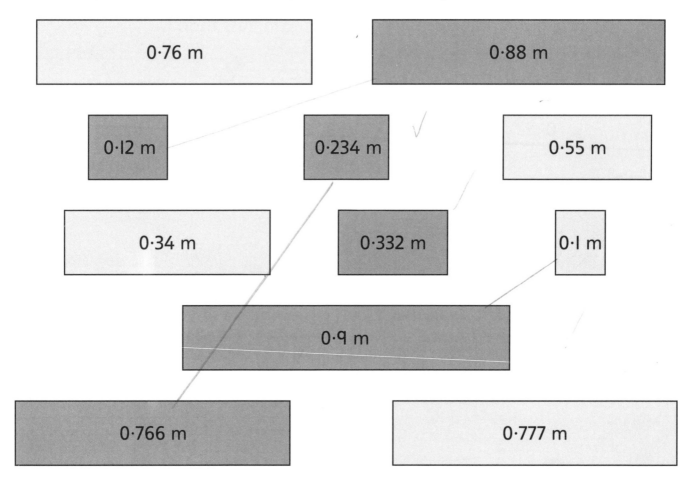

0·76 m

0·88 m

0·12 m

0·234 m

0·55 m

0·34 m

0·332 m

0·1 m

0·9 m

0·766 m

0·777 m

3 Lexi has made a number on a place value grid.

I need to add 0·84 to make 1.

Lexi

O	•	Tth	Hth
0̸ 9	•	0·1 0·1 2	0·01 0·01 0·01 0·01 0·01 0·01 6

What mistake has Lexi made?

What counters does she need to add?

_____

_____

4 **a)** Find the missing numbers.

i)

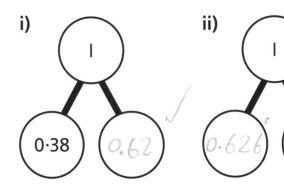

1

0·38   0.62 ✓

ii)

1

0.626   0·384

iii)

1

0·380   0·620 ✓

b) For part i) complete 4 number sentences.

0·38 + [0.62] = 1 ✓   [0.62] + [0.38] = 1

1 − [0.62] = [0.38] ✓   [1] − [0.62] = [0.38]

5 Complete the following.

a) 0·3 + [0.7] = 1 ✓   **d)** 0·90 + [0.1] = 1   **g)** 1 − 0·24 = [0.86]

b) 0·71 + [29] = 1   **e)** [0.223] + 0·787 = 1   **h)** 1 − [0.03] = 0·07

c) [0.05] + 0·05 = 1   **f)** 0·912 + [0.88] = 1   **i)** 1 − 0·235 = [0.775]

6 Work out the missing numbers.

a) $0.4 +$ [0.6] $= 1$ ✓

   $0.04 +$ [0.06] $= 1$

   $0.004 +$ [0.006] $= 1$

b) $0.4 +$ [0.6] $= 1$

   $0.40 +$ [0.6] $= 1$ ✓

   $0.400 +$ [0.6] $= 1$ ✓

---

7 **a)** Use six digits from 1, 3, 4, 5, 7, 8 to make two decimal numbers that add up to 1. You can use the same digit more than once but not within the same number.

CHALLENGE

O	·	Tth	Hth	Thth
0	·			
+ 0	·			
1	·	0	0	0

b) Find two different answers for part a).

What is the same and what is different about your answers?

_____

_____

Reflect

$$\begin{array}{r} 7\overset{1}{9}\overset{1}{3} \\ +\ 207 \\ \hline 1000 \end{array}$$

Andy says, '$0.207 + 0.793 = 1$.' Do you agree? Explain your answer.

Yes I do agree because I checked and it's correct ✓

Adding and subtracting decimals

12.05.22

1 Complete these decimal additions.

a) 0·37 + 0·82 = 1.19 ✓

O	•	Tth	Hth
	•	0·1 0·1 0·1	0·01 0·01 0·01 0·01 0·01 0·01 0·01
	•	0·1 0·1 0·1 0·1 0·1 0·1 0·1 0·1	0·01 0·01

O	·	Tth	Hth
0	·	3	7
+ 0	·	8	2
1	·	1	9

b) 0·675 + 0·721 = 1.396 ✓

O	•	Tth	Hth	Thth
	•	0·1 0·1 0·1 0·1 0·1 0·1	0·01 0·01 0·01 0·01 0·01 0·01 0·01	0·001 0·001 0·001 0·001 0·001
	•	0·1 0·1 0·1 0·1 0·1 0·1 0·1	0·01 0·01	0·001

O	·	Tth	Hth	Thth
0	·	6	7	5
+ 0	·	7	2	1
1	·	3	9	6

c) 0·56 + 0·78 = 1.34 ✓

O	·	Tth	Hth
0	·	5	6
+ 0	·	7	8
1	·	3	4

d) 0·7 + 0·7 = 1.4 ✓

O	·	Tth
0	·	7
+ 0	·	7
1	·	4

e) 0·82 + 0·78 = 1.6

O	·	Tth	Hth
0	·	8	2
+ 0	·	7	8
1	·	6	0

2 Match each calculation with its answer.

| 0·23 + 0·84 | 0·76 + 0·52 | 1 + 0·17 | 0·74 + 0·63 | 0·54 + 0·85 |

| 1·39 | 1·37 | 1·07 | 1·28 | 1·17 |

3 How much do the ruler and eraser cost altogether?

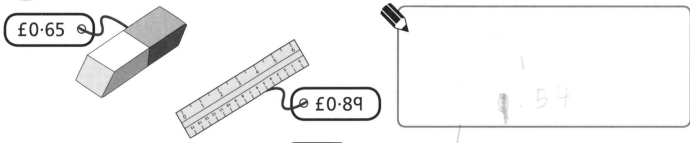

£0·65

£0·89

9.54

The ruler and eraser cost £ |1.54| altogether. ✓

4 Amal uses the treadmill at the gym.

He thinks he ran further on Thursday than he did from Monday to Wednesday in total. Is Amal correct?

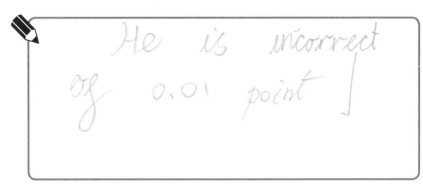

He is incorrect
of 0.01 point ✓

Day	Distance
Monday	0·625 km
Tuesday	0·193 km
Wednesday	0·208 km
Thursday	1·25 km

5 Write the missing numbers.

a)

O	·	Tth	Hth
0	·	4	3
+ 0	·	5	7
1	·	1	0

b)

O	·	Tth	Hth
0	·	8	8
+ 0	·	5	9
1	·	3	7

c)

O	·	Tth	Hth	Thth
0	·	7	3	2
+ 0	·	7	7	1
1	·	4	1	3

6 Use the signs <, = or > to complete each statement. Explain how you worked out your answers.

a) 0·51 + 0·63 ⟨ < ⟩ 0·51 + 0·73

1.11   1.24 ✓

b) 0·7 + 0·4 ⟨ = ⟩ 0·71 + 0·39 ✓

1.1   1.1

Reflect

Jamie says, '0·5 + 0·6 = 0·11.' Explain why Jamie is wrong.

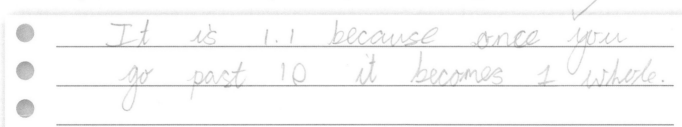

It is 1.1 because once you go past 10 it becomes 1 whole. ✓

Adding and subtracting decimals ⑤

1 There are some books for sale in
   a charity book shop.

12.05.22

Jed's Diary | Dictionary | Learn Spanish | Animals of the World

a) How much do the *Dictionary* and
   Animals of the World cost altogether?

| £3·79 | £6·50 | £5·76 | £4·31 |

O	•	Tth	Hth
① ① ① ① ① ①	•	0·1 0·1 0·1 0·1 0·1	
① ① ① ①	•	0·1 0·1 0·1	0·01

```
  O · Tth Hth
  6 · 5  0
+ 4 · 3  1
─────────
 10 · 8  1
```

The total cost is £ [10.81]. ✓

b) Work out the cost of *Learn Spanish* and *Jed's Diary*.

O	•	Tth	Hth
① ① ① ① ① ①	•	0·1 0·1 0·1 0·1 0·1 0·1 0·1	0·01 0·01 0·01 0·01 0·01 0·01
① ① ①	•	0·1 0·1 0·1 0·1 0·1 0·1 0·1	0·01 0·01 0·01 0·01 0·01 0·01 0·01 0·01 0·01

```
  O · Tth Hth
  5 · 7  6
+ 3 · 7  9
─────────
  9 · 5  5
```

The total cost is £ [9.55].

2 Complete the additions.

a) 2·3 + 4·6 = [6.9] ✓

```
  O · Tth
  2 · 3
+ 4 · 6
───────
  6 · 9
```

b) 3·5 + 5·8 = [9.3] ✓

```
  O · Tth
    ·
+   ·
───────
    ·
```

c) 1·98 + 0·77 = [2.75] ✓

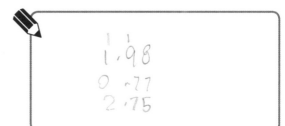

```
  1 1
  1·98
  0·77
  2·75
```

18

3 Work out the totals and use the >, < or = sign to complete each number sentence.

a) 0·502 + 4·165 ⟩ 3·258 + 0·875 ✓   b) 8·62 + 6·18 ⟩ 2·63 + 1·71 + 3·26

4 Zac wants to buy the scarf and the magazine.

T	O	.	Tth	Hth
	1	.	1	2
	3	.	6	9
	4	.	8	1

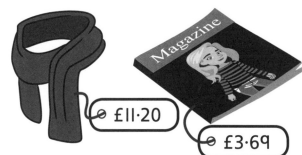

£11·20

£3·69

He adds the amounts.

What mistake has Zac made? What is the correct answer?

He put them in the wrong collom. it is 14/89 ✓

5 Find the answers. Mark them on the correct place on the number line.

4·5 + 2·8 = ☐   2·75 + 4·82 = ☐   1·823 + 6·077 = ☐

7   7·1   7·2   7·3   7·4   7·5   7·6   7·7   7·8   7·9   8·0

6) Reena's dad wants to take Reena and her little sister somewhere for her birthday. He has £50. Which activities can they afford to do?

CHALLENGE

	Theatre	Cinema	Zoo	Circus
Adult	£29·50	£15·69	£19·90	£16·60
Child	£9·75	£5·32	£12·50	£8·80

_____

_____

Reflect

Explain how to add 4·53 and 3·78.

_____

_____

_____

Adding and subtracting decimals ⑥

1 Danny buys a bottle of milk and loaf of bread.

The milk costs £1·05. The total cost of his items is £2·54

a) How much did the loaf of bread cost?

O	•	Tth	Hth

O	• Tth	Hth
2	· 5	4
− 1	· 0	5

The loaf of bread costs £ ⬜ .

b) Danny gives the shop keeper £2·70.

How much change does he get?

Danny gets £ ⬜ change.

2 Complete the subtractions.

a) 5·4 − 3·2 = ⬜   **b)** 7·26 − 4·83 = ⬜   **c)** 2·661 − 0·625 = ⬜

O	• Tth
5	· 4
− 3	· 2

O	• Tth Hth
	·
−	·

3 Complete the subtractions.

a) $7{\cdot}56 - 0{\cdot}49 = \boxed{}$

b) $12{\cdot}52 - 3{\cdot}92 = \boxed{}$

4 Kate has £6·20 in her pocket. She buys a bottle of water for 59p.

Kate does this calculation to work out her change.

What mistake has she made?

O	·	Tth	Hth
$^5\cancel{6}$	·	$^1 2$	0
− 0	·	5	9
5	·	7	9

_____

_____

_____

5 Holly is walking 24·5 km for charity. By 3 pm she has walked 18·7 km.

How much farther does Holly have to walk?

Holly has $\boxed{}$ km left to walk.

6 Complete the additions.

a) $3·21 + \boxed{} = 5·49$

b) $12·99 = \boxed{} + 5·32 + 2·69$

7 How much greater is the difference between A and C than the difference between B and C?

CHALLENGE

The difference between A and C is $\boxed{}$ greater than between B and C.

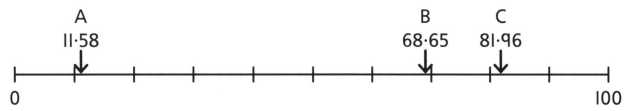

```
     A                              B      C
   11·58                          68·65  81·96
 ├────┼────┼────┼────┼────┼────┼────┼────┼────┤
 0                                              100
```

Reflect

What is the same and what is different about these calculations? Explain how you would work out the answer to each one.   a) $5·8 - 3·2$ b) $5·8 - 3·9$

Adding and subtracting decimals

1 Bella flies a paper plane 2·31 m. Ebo's paper plane flies 0·7 m.

How much further did Bella's paper plane fly?

Bella's plane flew ⬚ m further than Ebo's plane.

O	·	Tth	Hth
2	·	3	1
− 0	·	7	0
	·		

2 Work out the following calculations.

a) 3·62 + 4·8 = ⬚

O	·	Tth	Hth
3	·	6	2
− 4	·	8	
	·		

b) 1·96 − 1·258 = ⬚

O	·	Tth	Hth	Thth
1	·	9	6	
− 1	·	2	5	8
	·			

3 Complete the calculations.

a) 4·7 + 33·64 = ⬚

b) 9·5 + 1·872

4 a) $16\cdot9 - 11\cdot87 =$ ☐

b) $118\cdot7 - 3\cdot95 =$ ☐

5 Zac is working out $53\cdot49 - 3\cdot7$. Can you explain the mistake in his calculation? What is the correct answer?

T	O	.	Tth	Hth
5	3	.	4	9
−		3	.		7
5	0	.	4	2

_____

_____

$53\cdot49 - 3\cdot7 =$ ☐

6 Is Danny's statement true?

Answer always, sometimes or never.

_____

Give some examples to support your answer.

Subtracting a number with 2 decimal places from a number with 1 decimal place will give an answer with 2 decimal places.

Danny

7 Compare the number lines and find the difference between A and B.

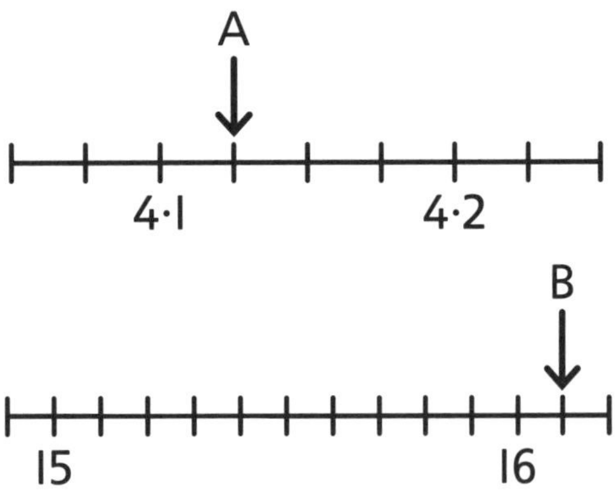

A

4·1   4·2

B

15   16

The difference between A and B is [ ].

8 These two cards have a difference of 1·55. What could the sum of the two cards be?

CHALLENGE

How many answers can you find?

19·7   [ ]

Reflect

What are the most important things to remember when adding or subtracting decimals with a different number of decimal places?

Adding and subtracting decimals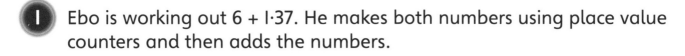

1 Ebo is working out 6 + 1·37. He makes both numbers using place value counters and then adds the numbers.

O	•	Tth	Hth
① ① ① ① ① ①	•		
①	•	0·1 0·1 0·1	0·01 0·01 0·01 0·01 0·01 0·01 0·01

```
  O · Tth Hth
  6 · 0   0
+ 1 · 3   7
_____
    ·
```

a) What answer did Ebo get? ☐

b) Explain a different way Ebo could find the answer.

_____

_____

2 All these calculations have the same answer. Find the missing numbers.

12 + 2·72 = ☐   5 + ☐·72 = ☐

3 + 11·☐ = ☐   0·72 + ☐ = ☐

5 + 5 + ☐ = ☐   14·7 + ☐ = ☐

3 Complete the column subtractions.

a) 7 – 3·8 = ☐

```
  O · Tth
  7 · 0
- 3 · 8
_____
    ·
```

b) 12 – 4·35 = ☐

```
T  O · Tth Hth
1  2 · 0   0
-    4 · 3   5
_____
     ·
```

4 Bella works out 5 – 2·84 by doing 4·99 – 2·83.

Use Bella's method to answer these calculations.

a) 8 – 2·807= [ ]　　**b)** 12 – 4·91 = [ ]　　**c)** 16 – 1·8 = [ ]

5 **a)** What is the total cost of these items?

£8　　£5　　£3·92

The total cost is £[ ]

b) Mary uses 18·7 ml of sun cream.

How much is left?

There is [ ] ml of sun cream left.

6 Work out the following calculations.

a) 3 + 0·45 = [ ]　　　　**d)** 2 + 9 + 3·4 = [ ]

b) 17 + 8·725 = [ ]　　　　**e)** 380 m + 70·85 m = [ ] m

c) 3·67 kg + 7 kg = [ ] kg　　**f)** 28·513 + 48 + 399 = [ ]

7 How much more milk than lemonade is there?

There is ☐ ml more milk than lemonade.

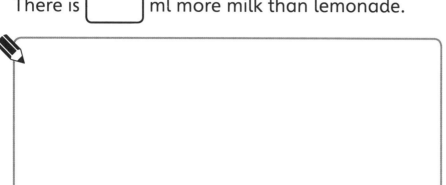

8 Work out the missing numbers.

CHALLENGE

a) $8 - 3.92 = 4 + $ ☐

b) $7.9 - 5.42 = 12 - $ ☐

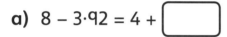

Reflect

How can you use a number line to show that $7 - 2.4$ is the same as $6.9 - 2.3$?

_____

_____

_____

Decimal sequences

16.05.22

1 Work out the missing numbers in each sequence.

a) 4·6, 4·7, 4·8, [4.9], [5], [5.1], [5.2] ✓

b) 11·5, 11·9, [12.3] ✓, 12·7, [13.1] ✓, 13·5, [13.9] ✓, [14.3] ✓

c) [15.75] ✓, [15.7] ✓, 15·65, 15·6, 15·55, [15.5] ✓, [15.45] ✓

2 Complete the numbers on the number line.

a)
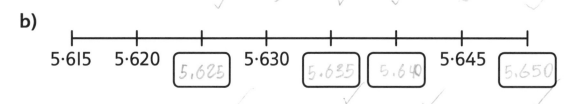

0·76   0·77   [0.78] ✓ [0.79] ✓ [0.8] ✓ [0.81] ✓ [0.82] ✓ [0.83] ✓

b)
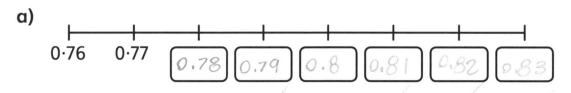

5·615   5·620   [5.625] ✓   5·630   [5.635] ✓ [5.640] ✓   5·645   [5.650] ✓

3 Kate is counting up by the same amount each time.

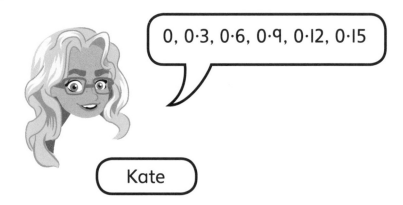

0, 0·3, 0·6, 0·9, 0·12, 0·15

Kate

What mistake has Kate made?

That after she gets to 10/1 she counts like this, 1.2, 1.5, 1.8...

4 Complete the sequence and write whether each rule is true or false.

a) 10·1, 10·3, 10·5, 10·7, [10.9]

The rule is 'add 0·2'.

_____True_____

c) 3·0, 2·25, 1·5, 0·75, [0.5]

The rule is 'subtract 0·25'.

_____False_____

b) 39·57, 39·60, 39·63, 39·66, [39.69]

The rule is 'add 0·3'.

_____True_____

d) 0·4, 0·52, 0·64, 0·76, [0.88]

The rule is 'add 0·12'.

_____True_____

5 Max is counting up by 0·02 each time. He starts at 12·45.

a) What are the next three numbers Max will say?

12·45, 12·47 ...

Max

17 . 53   17.55   17.57   17.59   17.

18.2

The next three numbers Max will say are [12.49] , [12.51] , [12.53].

b) Max stopped when he reached the first number above 18.

What number did Max stop on? [18.2]

6 Complete the sequences. Write the rule for each sequence.

a) 0·21, 0·42, 0·63, [0.84] , 1·05, 1·26, [1.47]

b) 11·3, [11.7] , 12·1, [12.5] , [12.9] , 13·3, 13·7

c) 7·68, 7·61, 7·54, 7·47, [7.4] , [7.33] , 7·26

Rules:	
a) goes up in 211	
b) goes up in 4	
c) goes down in 0.07	

7 Seven cones are spaced equally apart for a running race.

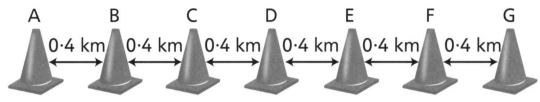

A   B   C   D   E   F   G
0·4 km 0·4 km 0·4 km 0·4 km 0·4 km 0·4 km

In round I, Toshi starts at A, runs to B and then back to A.

In round 2, he then runs from A to C and back to A.

He continues in the same pattern until round 6, when he runs A to G and back to A.

Complete the table to show how far Toshi runs each round and in total.

Round	I	2	3	4	5	6
Distance travelled in round (km)	0·4 Kim	0·8 Kim	0.12 Kim	0.16 Kim		
Total distance travelled so far (km)	0.8 Kim	0.16 Kim	0.24 Km	0.32 Kim		

Reflect

Make a sequence using decimal numbers. Ask a partner to continue the sequence. What rule did you use?

0.1, 0.2, 0.3, 0.4, 0.5, 0.6, 0.7, 0.8, 0.9

1, 1.1, 1.2, 1.3, 1.4, 1.5

the rule is to go up in 0.1

Problem solving – decimals ❶ 17.05.22

❶ Work out the missing values on the bar models.

a)

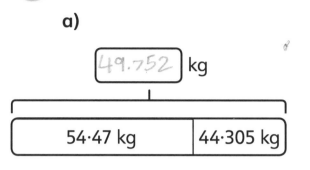

49.752 kg

| 54·47 kg | 44·305 kg |

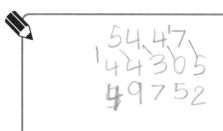

$$54.47$$
$$^1 44305$$
$$49752$$

b)

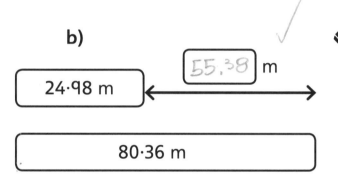

55.38 m

24·98 m

80·36 m

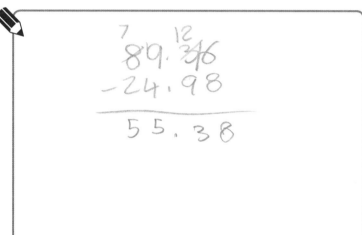

$$89.\overset{7}{\cancel{3}}\overset{12}{\cancel{4}}6$$
$$-24.98$$
$$55.38$$

c)

£28·98

| £ 1.28 | £12·67 | £15·03 |

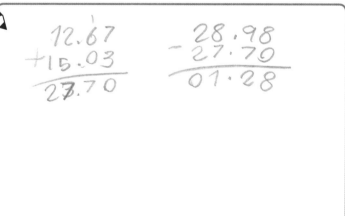

$$12.67$$
$$+15.03$$
$$27.70$$

$$28.98$$
$$-27.70$$
$$01.28$$

2 Toshi drives 26·3 km to work. He then drives 6·85 km to his gran's house.

How far does he drive in total?

$$\begin{array}{r} 6.85 \\ +\ 26.3 \\ \hline 8.48 \end{array}$$

Toshi drives ⬚8.48 km in total.

3 What is the mass of the grape?

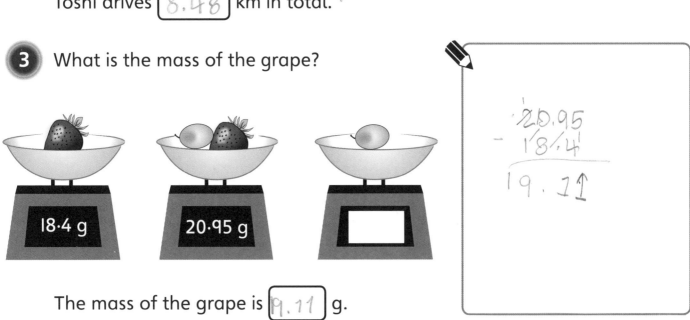

18·4 g   20·95 g

$$\begin{array}{r} 20.95 \\ -\ 18.4 \\ \hline 19.11 \end{array}$$

The mass of the grape is ⬚9.11 g.

4 Circle the two numbers that add up to 1·2 but have a difference of 0·78.

| 0·8 | 0·12 | 0·21 | 0·90 | 0·99 | 1·12 |

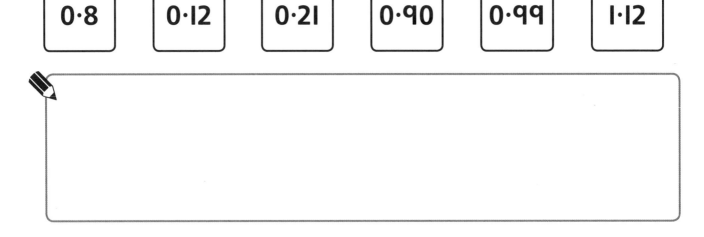

5 Complete the calculation.

$100 - 1·0 - 0·1 - 0·01 - 0·001 =$ $\boxed{88.99}$

90· 89,   88.9   88.99

6 Isla has £20. She spends £3·20 on a magazine. She then buys a book that costs £5·90 more than the magazine.

How much change should Isla receive in total?

CHALLENGE

10.90

$\begin{array}{r} {}^{1}5.90 \\ + 3.20 \\ \hline 9.10 \end{array}$

$\begin{array}{r} {}^{1}20.100 \\ - 9.10 \\ \hline 10.90 \end{array}$

Reflect

Look at the bar models in question 1. Write a question that you could solve using one of the bar models.

1235

350   540   ?   = 345

$\begin{array}{r} 350 \\ +540 - \\ \hline 890 \end{array}$

$\begin{array}{r} {}^{0\ 11}1235 \\ - 890 \\ \hline 345 \end{array}$

Problem solving – decimals ❷

1   Amelia buys three items.

How much do the three items cost in total?

17.05.22

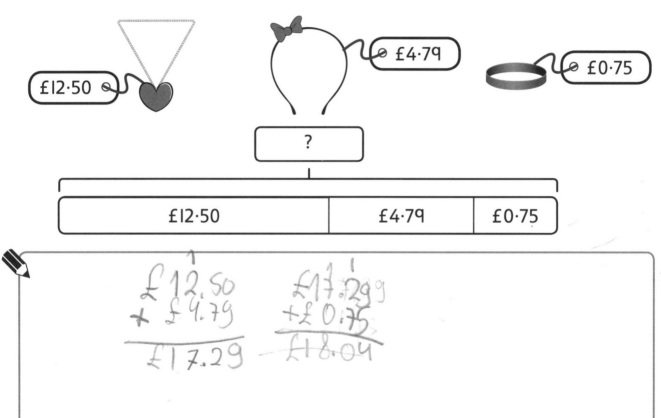

£12·50   £4·79   £0·75

| £12·50 | £4·79 | £0·75 |

Working shown:

£12.50
+ £4.79
_____
£17.29

£17.29
+£0.75
_____
£18.04

The total cost of the three items is £ [£18.04].

2   Danny buys two items for his dog. He buys a chew toy costing £4·67 and a lead that costs £2·85 more than the chew toy. He pays with a £20 note.

How much change does Danny get?

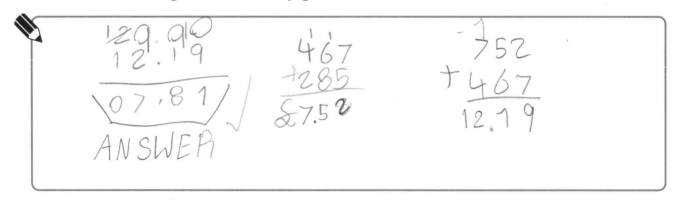

20.00
12.19
_____
07.81
ANSWER

467
+285
_____
£7.52

752
+467
_____
12.19

3 A bucket has 8·75l l of water in it. Amal pours a further 7·5 l into the bucket. l·27 l of water spill out because the bucket is full.

How much water does the bucket hold?

4 Choose three numbers from the cards that make the calculation true.

☐ + ☐ − ☐ = 10

| 0·345 | 2·233 | 3·578 | 8·655 | 12·178 |

5 Three identical rectangles are put together with their edges touching.

What is the length of the side marked A?

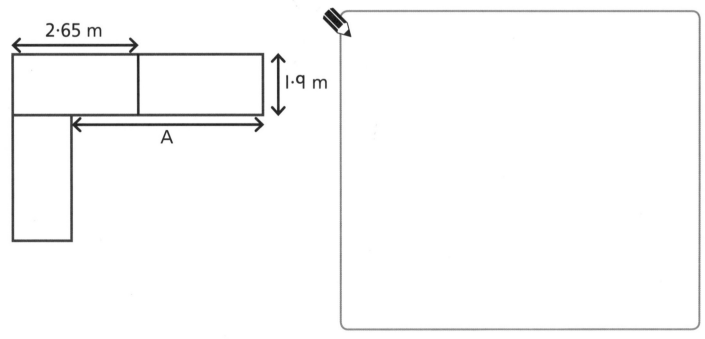

2·65 m

1·9 m

A

6 When added together, these two cards total 9·2.

What is the difference between the cards?

4·59	

7 Kate and Richard have both saved some money.

CHALLENGE

Richard needs to save another £1·20 to make £100.

After paying £24·78 for stationery, Kate has £36·98 less than Richard. How much more money has Richard saved than Kate?

Reflect

Write a problem-solving question with the answer 3·21 kg. Ask your partner to check the answer.

Multiplying decimals by 10 18.05.22

1 Use the place value grids to help you complete these multiplications.

a) $2·4 \times 10 =$ **24**

b) $0·13 \times 10 =$ **13**

T	O	•	Tth
		•	

O	•	Tth	Hth
	•		

2 Complete the multiplications.

a) $1·3 \times 10 =$ **13**

H	T	O	•	Tth	Hth	Thth
		1	•	3		
			•			

c) $13·5 \times 10 =$ **135**

H	T	O	•	Tth	Hth	Thth
		1	3	•	5	
				•		

b) $1·35 \times 10 =$ **135**

H	T	O	•	Tth	Hth	Thth
		1	•	3	5	
			•			

d) $0·135 \times 10 =$ **135**

H	T	O	•	Tth	Hth	Thth
		0	•	1	3	5
			•			

39

3 Olivia says, '14·8 × 10 = 14·80.'

What mistake has Olivia made?

What is the correct answer?

The correct answer is 148.

4 Draw lines to match each multiplication to its answer.

| 0·003 × 10 | 3·53 × 10 | 0·03 × 10 | 10 × 0·353 | 0·3 × 10 | 10 × 3·003 | 0·0353 × 10 |

0·03   3   35·3   30·03   0·353   0·3   3·53

5 Complete the multiplications.

a) 5·8 × 10 = $\boxed{58}$ h) 0·019 × 10 = $\boxed{0.19}$

b) 5·82 × 10 = $\boxed{582}$ i) $\boxed{0.309}$ = 3·09 × 10

c) 24·9 × 10 = $\boxed{249}$ j) 0·04 × 10 = $\boxed{0.4}$

d) 1·09 × 10 = $\boxed{109}$ k) $\boxed{3099}$ = 3·099 × 10

e) 21·08 × 10 = $\boxed{2108}$ l) 0·004 × 10 = $\boxed{0.04}$

f) 0·198 × 10 = $\boxed{198}$ m) $\boxed{3099}$ = 30·99 × 10

g) 10 × 21·08 = $\boxed{2108}$ n) 0·040 × 10 = $\boxed{0.40}$

6 **a)** Luis is working out the missing number in $\boxed{125}$ × 10 = 12·5.

He thinks the missing number is 125. Is Luis correct? Explain your answer.

Yes he is correct because that I worked it out.

b) Work out the missing numbers.

$\boxed{1.5}$ × 10 = 15 $\boxed{92}$ × 10 = 9·2 $\boxed{173}$ × 10 = 1·73

$\boxed{2.5}$ × 10 = 25   10 × $\boxed{152}$ = 15·2 $\boxed{173}$ × 10 = 17·3

7 Mo's stride is 0·8 metres long. Lexi's stride is 0·65 metres long. They each take 20 strides.

How much further has Mo travelled than Lexi?

$$\begin{array}{r} 5\ \overset{6}{\cancel{}}\overset{15}{\cancel{}} \\ -\ \ \ 8 \\ \hline 5\ 7 \end{array}$$

Mo has travelled $\boxed{57}$ m further than Lexi.

Reflect

Explain what happens to the digits when you multiply a decimal number by 10.

Multiplying decimals by 10, 100 and 1,000

1 Complete the place value grids to work out the answers. 1805.22

a)

$7·9 \times 10 \quad = \boxed{79}$

$7·9 \times 100 \quad = \boxed{790}$

$7·9 \times 1,000 = \boxed{7900}$

Th	H	T	O	•	Tth	Hth
			7	•	9	
				•		
				•		
				•		

b)

$2·19 \times 10 \quad = \boxed{219}$

$2·19 \times 100 \quad = \boxed{2190}$

$2·19 \times 1,000 = \boxed{21900}$

Th	H	T	O	•	Tth	Hth
			2	•	1	9
				•		
				•		
				•		

c) $0·84 \times 100 = \boxed{84}$

Th	H	T	O	•	Tth	Hth
			0	•	8	4
			8	•	4	

e) $0·05 \times 100 = \boxed{500}$

Th	H	T	O	•	Tth	Hth
		0	5	•	0	0
			5	•	0	0

d) $0·7 \times 1,000 = \boxed{7000}$

Th	H	T	O	•	Tth	Hth
			0	•	7	
		7	0	•	0	0

f) $1,000 \times 1·7$

Th	H	T	O	•	Tth	Hth
			1	•	7	
		7	0	•	0	0

2 Complete the calculations.

a) $0.4 \times 100 =$ 40

$0.04 \times 100 =$ 400

$0.004 \times 100 =$ 4000

$100 \times 0.4 =$ 40

b) $1.7 \times 100 =$ 1,70

$1.7 \times 1,000 =$ 1700

$0.17 \times 1,000 =$ 17,000

c) 91209 $\times 100 = 912$

91200 $\times 100 = 91.2$

912000 $\times 1,000 = 9.12$

$1,000 \times$ 9.12 $= 91.2$

d) $4.5 \times$ 100 $= 450$

$0.045 \times$ 1000 $= 4.5$

$0.045 \times$ 100 $= 0.45$

$0.045 \times$ 10 $= 45$

3 a) sophia grape Sofia buys 1,000 cans of orange juice for the school café. One can contains 0.335 litres of juice. sophia grape

How many litres of orange juice did Sofia buy?

3335 is the answer

b) The length of a blue straw is 0.11 m. The length of a red straw is 0.09 m.

What is the total length of 100 blue and 100 red straws?

④ Complete the missing numbers in this multiplication grid.

Number	12	112	0·38	7691	0·012
× 100	1.2	3·6	380	76·91	0.12
× 1000	12·07	36	38.00	76.91	1·2

⑤ Use the number cards to find three ways to complete each calculation.

CHALLENGE

| 10 | 100 | 1,000 | 6·8 | 0·68 | 0·068 |

a) [ ] × [ ] = 68   b) [ ] × [ ] = [ ] × [ ]

[ ] × [ ] = 68   [ ] × [ ] = [ ] × [ ]

[ ] × [ ] = 68   [ ] × [ ] = [ ] × [ ]

Reflect

● Complete the sentences:

● • Multiplying by 100 is the same as multiplying by [10] and [10] again.

● • Multiplying by 1,000 is the same as multiplying by [250] and [250] and [250] again.

● Show your partner how you can use a place value grid to multiply by 100 or 1,000.

Dividing decimals by 10

19.05.22

1 Use the place value grids to help you work out the divisions.

$1.2 \div 10 = \boxed{0.12}$

O	•	Tth	Hth
①	•	(0·1)(0·1)	

O	•	Tth	Hth
	•	(0·1)(0·1)(0·1)(0·1)(0·1)(0·1)(0·1)(0·1)(0·1)(0·1)	(0·01)

T	O	•	Tth	Hth
	1	•	2	
		•		

2 Work out these divisions.

a) $4.5 \div 10 = \boxed{0.45}$

Th	H	T	O	•	Tth	Hth
			4	•	5	
				•		

c) $45 \div 10 = \boxed{4.5}$

Th	H	T	O	•	Tth	Hth
		4	5	•		
				•		

b) $0.45 \div 10 = \boxed{0.045}$

Th	H	T	O	•	Tth	Hth
				•		
				•		

d) $4.52 \div 10 = \boxed{0.452}$

Th	H	T	O	•	Tth	Hth
				•		
				•		

3 What number should go in each part of the bar?

2·31

| ? | ? | ? | ? | ? | ? | ? | ? | ? | ? |

23,1 ÷ 10 = 2,31

4 10 apples have a total mass of 2·8 kg. Each of the apples has the same mass.

What is the mass of one apple?

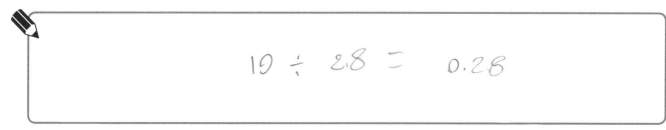

10 ÷ 2,8 = 0.28

The mass of one apple is 0.28 kg.

5 Work out the following missing numbers.

a) 603 ÷ 10 = 6,03   d) 75·3 ÷ 10 = 7·53   g) 0·035 = 0,0035 ÷ 10

b) 160·3 ÷ 10 = 16,03   e) 0.8 ÷ 10 = 0·08   h) 8·719 = 0,8719 ÷ 10

c) 16·31 ÷ 10 = 1,631   f) 3·978 ÷ 10 = 0,3978   i) 3·895 × 10 = 384,5 ÷ 10
38,95

6 Is Max correct? Explain any mistakes.

_____

_____

_____

_____

_____

10 books costs £35, so each book costs £3·5.

Max

7 **a)** What is the cost of 100 ml of lemonade?

100 ml of lemonade costs £ [0.0180] . 0.0180 ÷ 100 =

b) What is the cost of 200 g of cocoa?
Explain your answer.

200 g of cocoa costs £ [0.0012] .

0.0012 ÷ 100

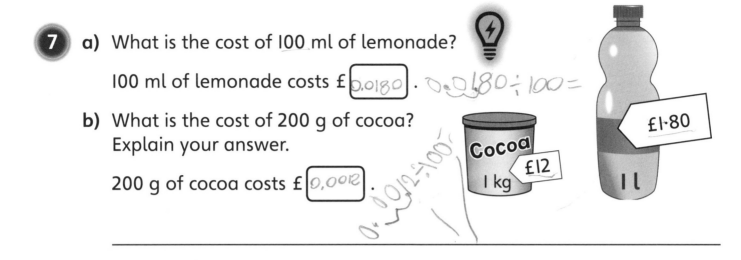

£1·80

Cocoa £12
1 kg

1 l

_____

_____

8 Toshi has 2·5 kg of hot chocolate powder. He makes 10 cups of hot chocolate every week for 10 weeks before it runs out.

How much does he use in each cup? Give your answer in kg.

0.025

Toshi uses [0.025] kg of hot chocolate powder in each cup.

CHALLENGE

Reflect

Explain how to divide a decimal number by 10.

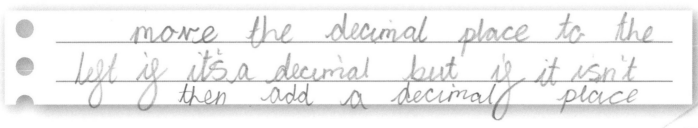

move the decimal place to the left if it's a decimal but if it isn't then add a decimal place

Dividing decimals by 10, 100 and 1,000

1 Use the place value grids to answer these questions.

a) 23 ÷ 100 = 0.23 ✓

H	T	O	•	Tth	Hth	Thth
	2	3	•			
			•			

c) 5·2 ÷ 100 = 0.052 ✓

H	T	O	•	Tth	Hth	Thth
		5	•	2		
			•			

b) 145 ÷ 1,000 = 0.0145 ✓

H	T	O	•	Tth	Hth	Thth
			•			
			•			

d) 13 ÷ 1,000 = 0.013

H	T	O	•	Tth	Hth	Thth
			•			
			•			

2 Use the tenths grid to show if Bella is correct.

Explain your answer.

> Dividing by 10 and then 10 again is the same as dividing by 100.
>
> Bella

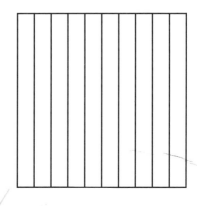

Yes she is correct. ✓
Because there are 2 0's in
both 10ˢ which is like 100.

48

3 Write true or false under each calculation. Correct those that are incorrect.

a) $9 \div 100 = 0.09$

True ✓

c) $53 \div 100 = 0.053$

True

e) $8.7 \div 100 = 0.87$

False ✓

b) $7 \div 1,000 = 0.007$

False

d) $75 \div 1,000 = 0.075$

True

f) $9.1 \div 1,000 = 0.00091$

_0.091_ ✓

4 Draw lines to match the calculations that give the same answer. Not all have a pair.

_0.008_

| $0.8 \div 100$ | $0.18 \div 100$ | $10.8 \div 100$ | $0.108 \div 10$ |

| $108 \div 1,000$ | $0.08 \div 100$ | $8 \div 1,000$ | $1.8 \div 1,000$ | $1.08 \div 100$ |

5 Complete the calculations.

a) $3.7 \div \boxed{10} = 0.37$ ✓

$3.7 \div \boxed{100} = 0.037$

$3.7 \div \boxed{1000} = 0.0037$

b) $\boxed{1.2} \div 10 = 0.12$ ✓

$\boxed{12} \div 100 = 0.12$

$\boxed{120} \div 1,000 = 0.12$ ✓

49

6 Each day Zac and Jamie put some money in their money box.

After 100 days Zac has £18 and Jamie has £124.

If they always put in the same amount each day, how much more money did Jamie save each day in pounds?

Jamie saved £ [ ] more each day.

---

7 Each shape represents a different number. Find the missing values.

CHALLENGE

$■ \div 10 = ▲ \times 100 = 0.098$

$★ \times 10 = 0.61 \div 100 = ●$

$■ =$ [ ]

$▲ =$ [ ]

$★ =$ [ ]

$● =$ [ ]

Reflect

Reena thinks that $0.351 \div 10 = 3.51 \div 100$ and $3.51 \div 100 = 35.1 \div 1{,}000$.
Is Reena correct? Explain your answer.

End of unit check

My journal

1 Max is working out 12 − 4·35.

a) Show two different ways Max could do this.

What advice would you give Max?

_____

_____

b) What mistakes should Max be careful not to make when subtracting decimals?

_____

_____

2 What is the same and what is different about these calculations?

25 + 2·95   12·47 + 13·48   18·3 + 9·65

Power check

How do you feel about your work in this unit?

Power play

The aim is to find a path from 2 to 0·002.

How many different paths can you find? Use the place value grid to help you.

TTh	Th	H	T	O	•	Tth	Hth	Thth
					•			
					•			

2	÷ 100	÷ 10	× 100	× 10	÷ 100
÷ 1,000	× 100	× 10	÷ 10	× 100	× 10
× 10	÷ 100	× 10	÷ 10	× 100	÷ 1,000
× 100	÷ 10	× 1,000	× 100	× 10	0·002

Now find a route where the answer is 2!

2	÷ 100	÷ 10	× 100	× 10	÷ 100
÷ 1,000	× 100	× 10	÷ 10	× 100	× 10
× 10	÷ 100	× 10	÷ 10	× 100	÷ 1,000
× 100	÷ 10	× 1,000	× 100	× 10	2

Explain your method.

_____

_____

Measuring angles in degrees

08.06.22

1 **a)** Tick the diagrams that show a 180-degree turn.

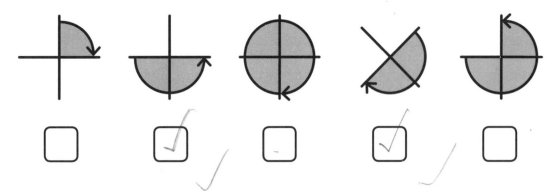

☐   ☑   ☐   ☑   ☐

b) Tick the diagrams that show 90-degree turns.

☑   ☐   ☑   ☐   ☐   ☑

c) Describe each turn using degrees, and 'clockwise' or 'anticlockwise'.

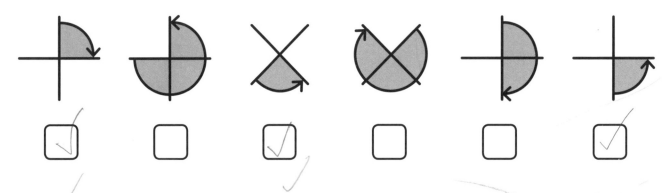

i) [360]° _clock_ wise

iii) [180]° _anticlock_ wise

v) [270]° _clockwise_ wise

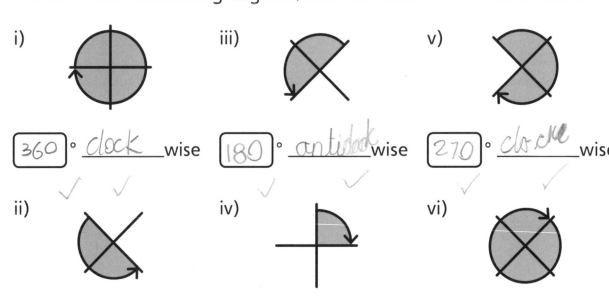

ii) [180]° _anticlock_ wise

iv) [90]° _clock_ wise

vi) [360]° _clock_ wise

2 Complete the table for the different turns the ship makes.

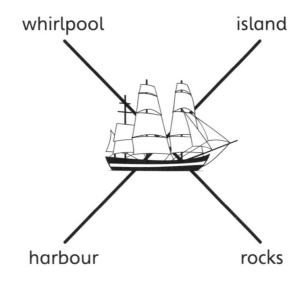

whirlpool   island

harbour   rocks

Starts facing	Turns	Now facing
whirlpool	90° clockwise	island ✓
harbour	180° clockwise	island ✓
island	270 ° anticlockwise	rocks
island ✓	360° clockwise ✓	island
harbour	270° clockwise	whirlpool

3 Describe each turn in degrees clockwise or anticlockwise.

a) Turn from B to F   180 ° clockwise ✓

b) Turn from H to B   90 ° clockwise ✓

c) Turn from C to D   45 ° clockwise ✓

d) Turn from D to A   270 ° clockwise ✓

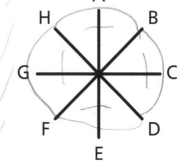

4 A robot has two buttons.

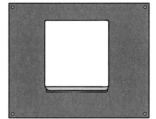

This button makes the robot turn 270° clockwise. *3x 90*

This button makes it turn 45° anticlockwise. *half of 90*

The robot is facing C and needs to face D.

Describe different combinations of button pushes you could use to make the robot complete this turn.

Which combination requires the fewest button pushes?

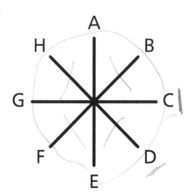

You would need to push the square and then the triangle three times to get to D with the fewest 4 presses

Reflect

Draw diagrams to show turns of 90°, 180°, 270° and 45°.

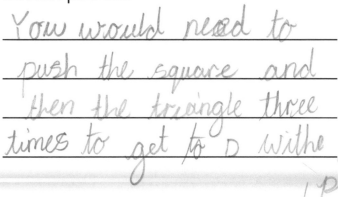

Measuring with a protractor ❶

09.06.22

1 How many degrees is each turn?

a)

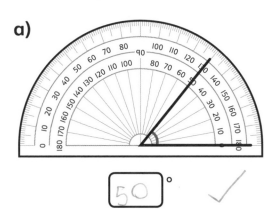

50 ° ✓

c)

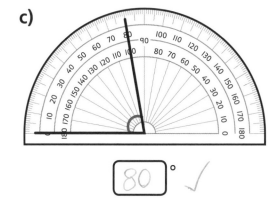

80 ° ✓

b)

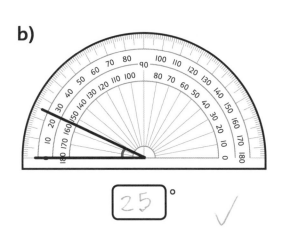

25 ° ✓

d)

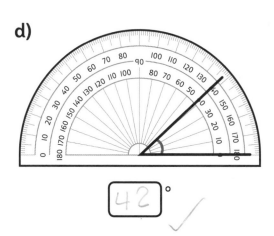

42 ° ✓

2 Measure each angle using a protractor.

a)

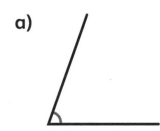

110 °

c)

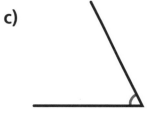

65 °

b)

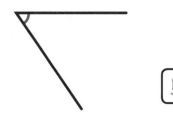

55 ° ✓

d)

130 °

57

3 Measure the angles in these triangles.

a)

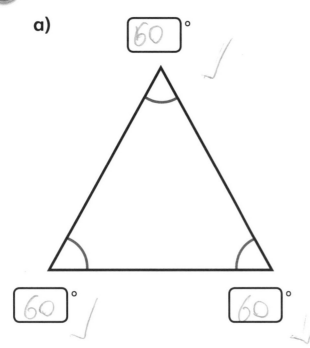

60 °

60 °   60 °

b)

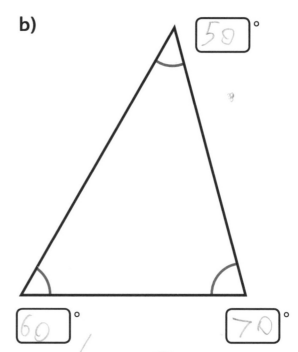

50 °

60 °   70 °

4 Explain the mistakes Richard and Emma have made.

a)

Richard

This angle is 120°.

He has to start from 0.

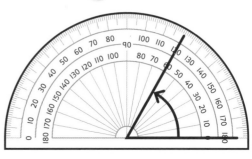

b)

Emma

This angle is 40°.

If it the angle is to the right then you would count the very top number.

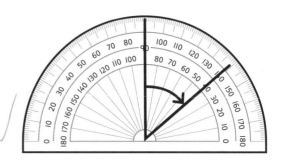

5 Isla says: 'I cannot measure these angles because some of the lines are too short.'

CHALLENGE

Find a way to measure these angles accurately and write the measurement beneath each angle.

a)

☐ °

b)

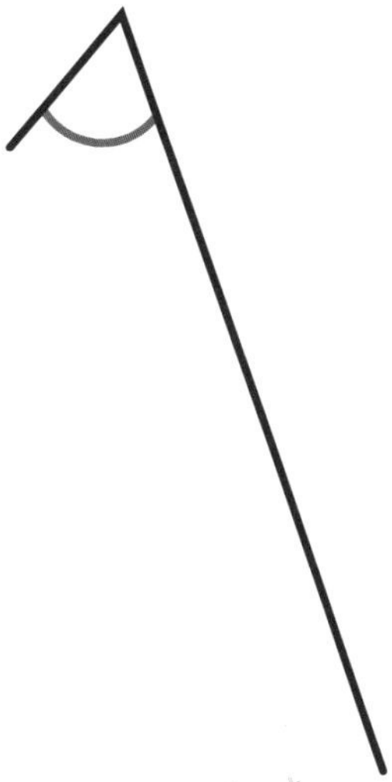

730 °

c)

☐ °

Reflect

Explain the most important steps when measuring an angle with a protractor.

Measuring with a protractor ❷

1 Tick the protractors that have been placed correctly on the angles.

a)

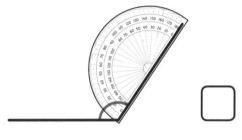

☐

c)

☑

b)

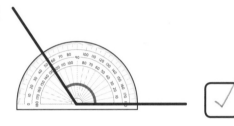

☑

d)

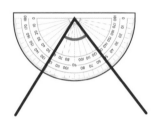

☐

2 Measure these angles accurately using a protractor.

a)

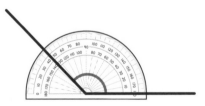

$\boxed{45}$ °

c)

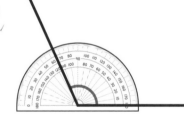

$\boxed{65}$ °

b)

$\boxed{65}$ °

d)

$\boxed{130}$ °

3 Put these angles in order, from greatest to smallest.

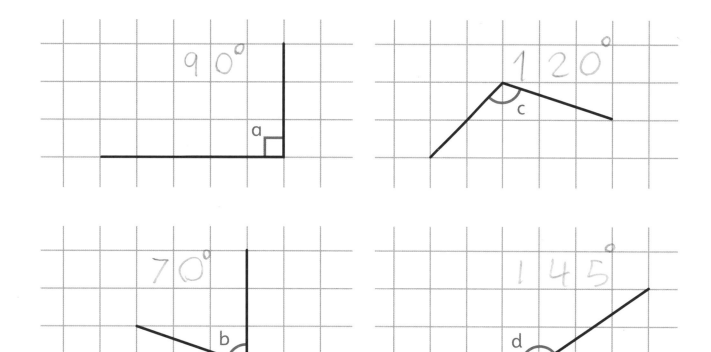

Greatest turn | D | C | a | b | Smallest turn

✓ ✓ ✓ ✓

4 Measure the obtuse angles in these shapes.

a)

b)

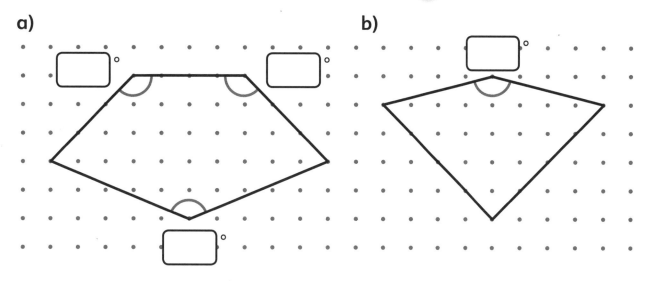

5 Max stands at marker X. He turns to face different markers.

Measure the angles he turns and complete the table.

CHALLENGE

Turns clockwise from:	Angle of turn
A to F	
F to I	
I to B	
B to G	
G to I	

B
A
C
I
X
D
F
E
H
G

Reflect

How do you know which scale to read on a protractor when measuring an obtuse angle?

14.06.22

Drawing lines and angles accurately

1 Complete the angles by adding another line.

a) Draw a 60° angle. *acute*

✓

b) Draw a 120° angle. *obtuse*

c) Draw a 30° angle. *acute*

✓

d) Draw a 90° angle. *right angle*

✓

2 Draw two more different angles showing 100° in different orientations.

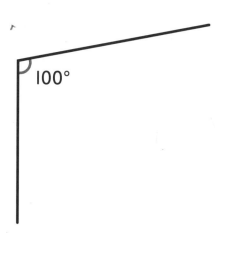

100°

a)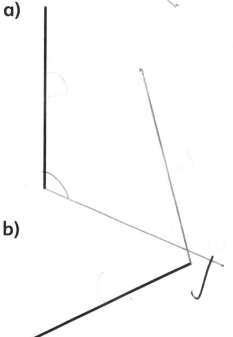

b)

3 Copy each step to complete the design below. Use your drawing to calculate the missing length and angles.

The diagrams are not to scale.

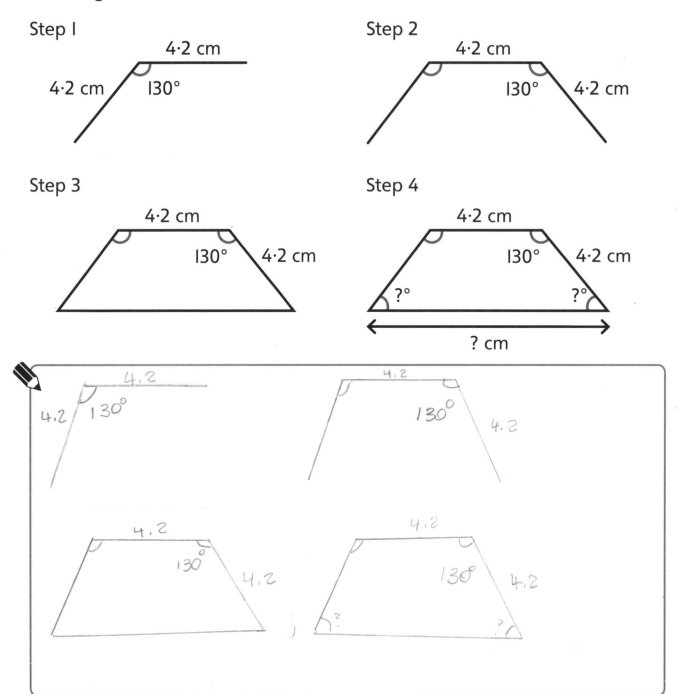

Step I

4·2 cm

4·2 cm   130°

Step 2

4·2 cm

130°   4·2 cm

Step 3

4·2 cm

130°   4·2 cm

Step 4

4·2 cm

130°   4·2 cm

?°   ?°

? cm

The missing length is ⬚ 9,5 ⬚ cm.

The missing angles are ⬚ 50 ⬚° and ⬚ 50 ⬚°.

4 Draw a triangle with angles of 45°, 60° and 75°.

Are all of the sides the same length?

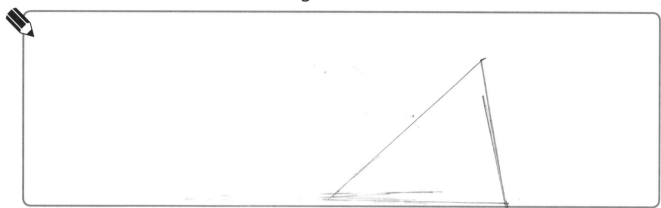

5 Draw a triangle with three angles of 60°. Make each side 3 cm long.

CHALLENGE

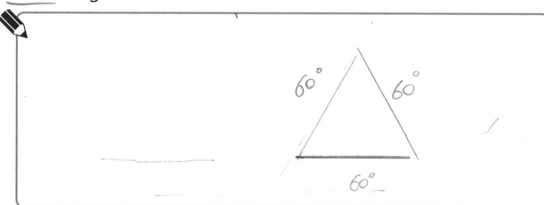

Reflect

Draw three different angles showing exactly 45°.

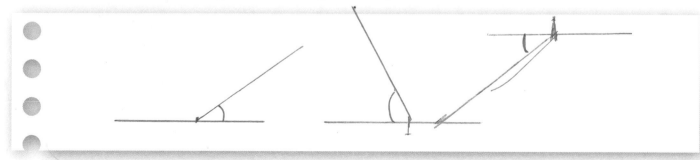

65

Calculating angles on a straight line

1 Calculate the size of the missing angles, then measure to test your prediction.

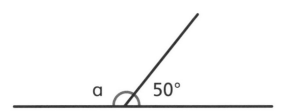 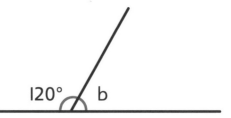

a) I predict a is ⬚° because 180 – ⬚ = ⬚ .

b) I predict b is ⬚° because 180 – ⬚ = ⬚ .

2 Calculate the missing angles.

a)

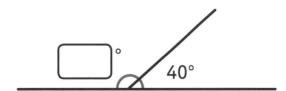

c)

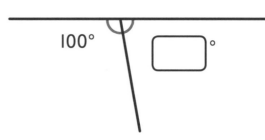

b)

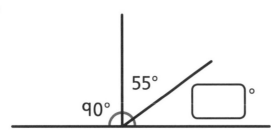

d)

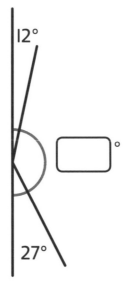

3 **a)** Find two pairs that join together to make a straight line.

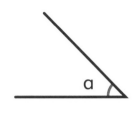

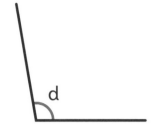

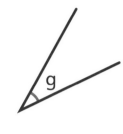

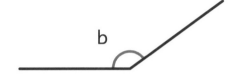

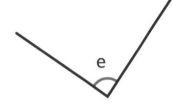

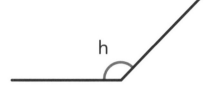

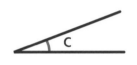

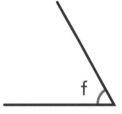

_____ and _____ or _____ and _____

b) Find three angles that join together to make a straight line.

_____ and _____ and _____

4 Find the missing angles.

a)

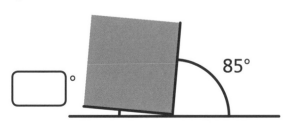

85°

b)

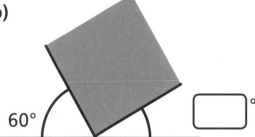

60°

5 All the angles labelled a are of equal size. All the angles labelled b are of equal size. All the angles labelled c are of equal size.

Calculate the size of the angle labelled '?'.

? = [ ]°

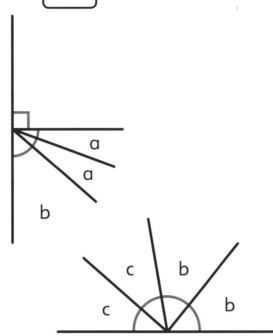

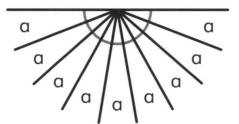

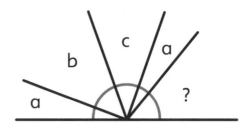

Reflect

Aki says 'The missing angle must be 45°, because 45 + 45 is a right angle, then you just add on the other hundred.'

Explain Aki's mistake.

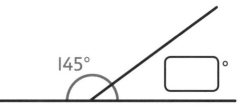

145°

[ ]°

Calculating angles around a point 20.06.22

1 Find the missing angles.

a)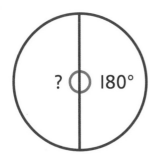

b)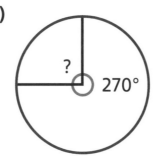

c)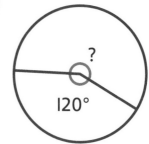

$360° - \boxed{180}° = \boxed{180}°$ $360° - \boxed{270}° = \boxed{90}°$ $360° - \boxed{120}° = \boxed{240}°$

2 Calculate the missing angles.

a)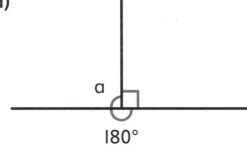

Angle a is $\boxed{90}°$.

b)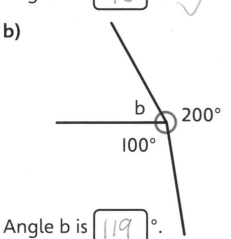

Angle b is $\boxed{119}°$.

c)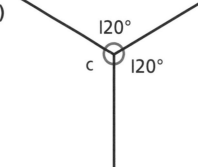

Angle c is $\boxed{120}°$.

d)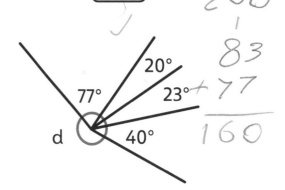

Angle d is $\boxed{200}°$.

$$\begin{array}{r} 360 \\ - 160 \\ \hline 200 \end{array}$$

$$\begin{array}{r} 83 \\ + 77 \\ \hline 160 \end{array}$$

69

3 **a)** Draw an angle of 250°.

^{1250}
-180
70

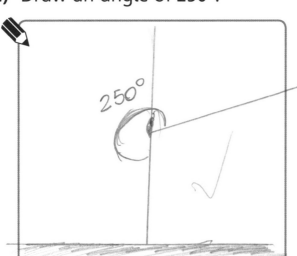

b) Draw an angle of 350°.

$^315 0$
-180
170

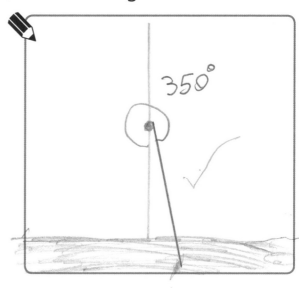

4 Max turns 170° then a further 85°.

He makes one final turn and he is facing where he started. What angle did he turn?

Max turned 255°.

5 Explain why what Reena says is incorrect.

Reena

I will split this into four obtuse angles.

Because a circle is 360° and an obtuse angle is anything above 90° to anything under 180°.

6 These angles have been split into angles of equal size.

Find the size of each angle.

CHALLENGE

a)

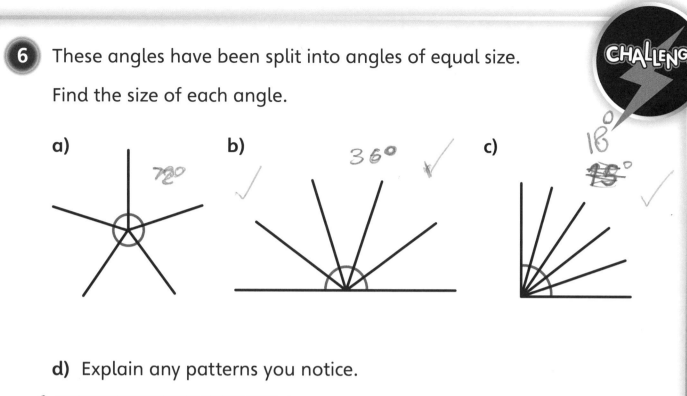

720

b)

360 ✓

c)

18°
15° ✓

d) Explain any patterns you notice.

Reflect

There are three angles that make a whole turn. One of the angles is 110°.
What could the other two angles be?

125° and 125°   360
                − 110
                ─────
                 250

                 125
               2)250

✓

Calculating lengths and angles in shapes

1 Calculate the interior angles of each shape.   21.06.22

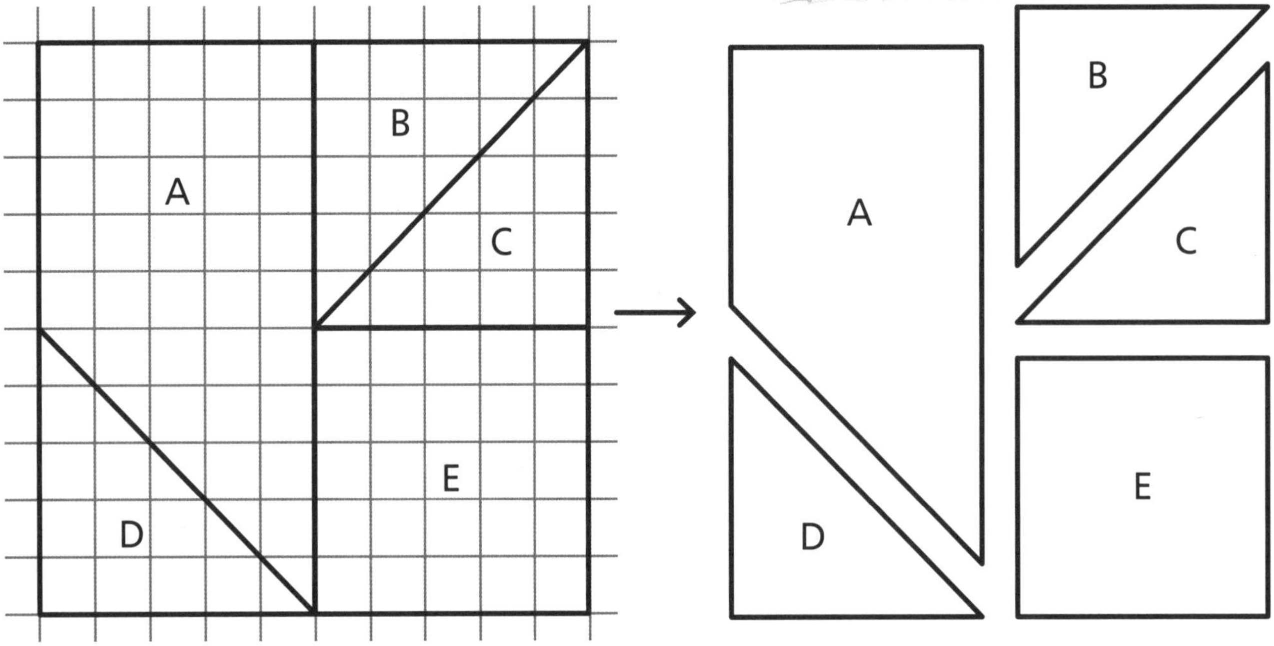

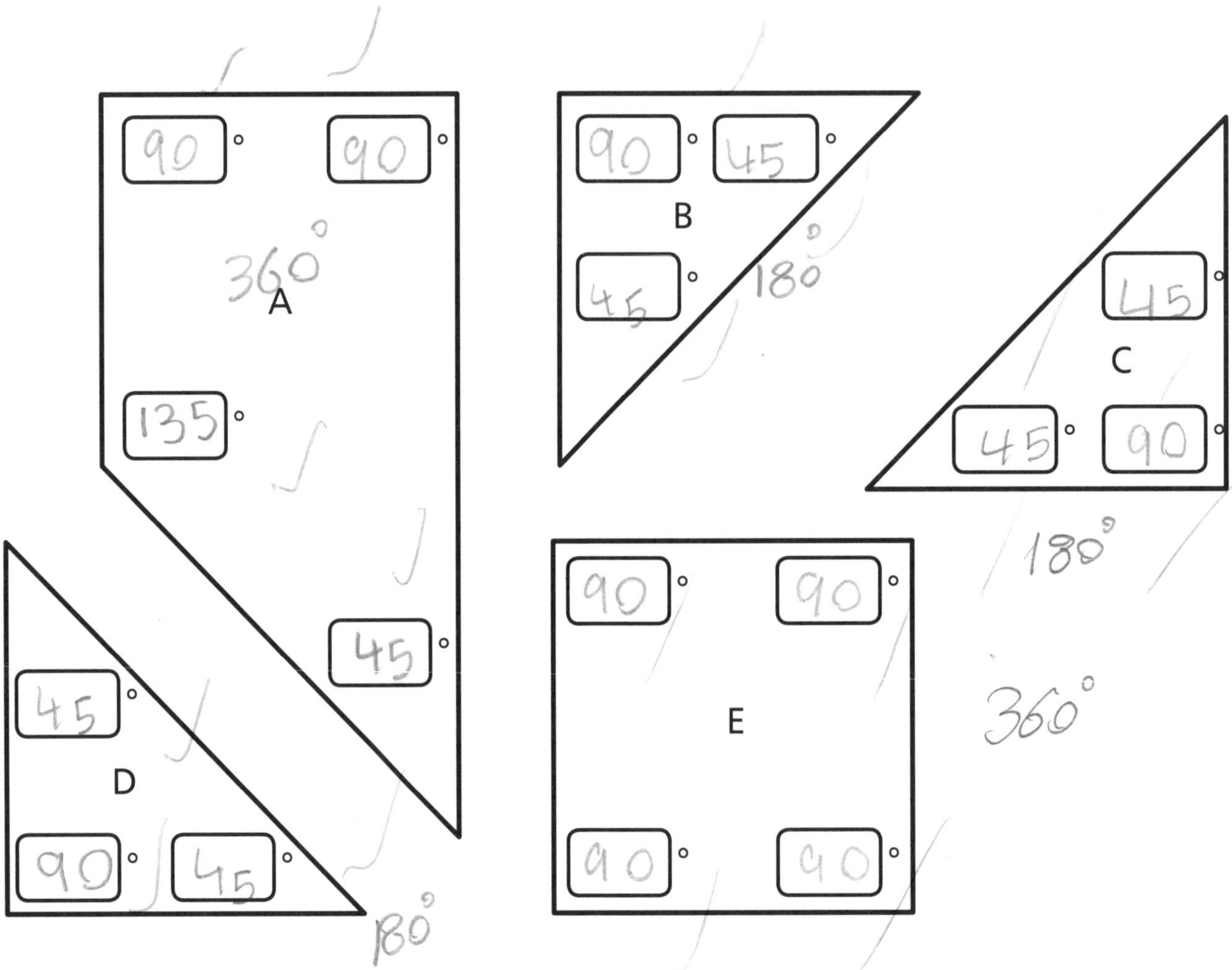

Shape A: 90° 90° 135° 45° / 360°

Shape B: 90° 45° 45° / 180°

Shape C: 45° 45° 90° / 180°

Shape D: 45° 90° 45° / 180°

Shape E: 90° 90° 90° 90° / 360°

2 Find the missing lengths and the marked angles.

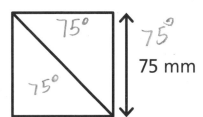

a)

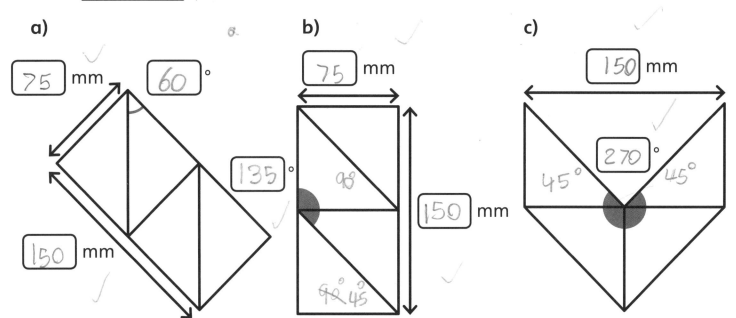

75 mm   60 °

150 mm   135 °

b)

75 mm

98

92 45

150 mm

c)

150 mm

270 °

45°   45°

3 Calculate the missing angles.

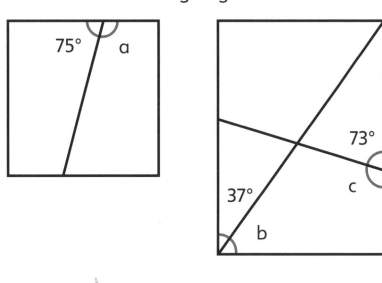

75°   a

73°

c

37°

b

a = 5 °   b = 43 °   c = 7 °

4 The outline shape below is made up of six of these triangles.

Find the values of a, b and c.

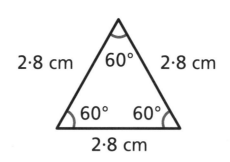

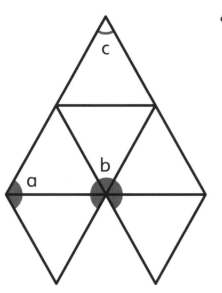

a = 120 °   b = 300 °   c = 60 °

Reflect

'It is better to calculate rather than measure missing angles.'

Do you agree with this statement? Explain your answer.

I think that is correct because it is easier for me to do.

End of unit check

My journal

 a

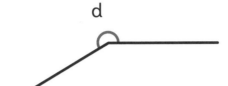 d

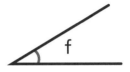 f

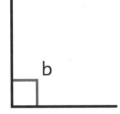 b

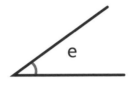 e

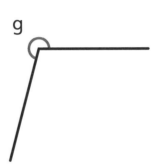 g

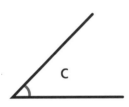 c

a) Which groups of angles could fit together to form a whole turn?

b) Which groups of angles could fit together to form a straight line?

75

2 Use measuring and calculation to find the angles where the grey square touches the larger square.

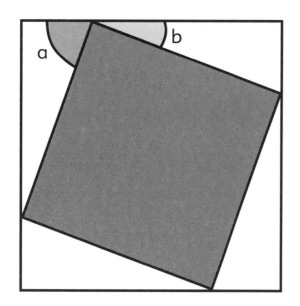

$a = \boxed{}°$

$b = \boxed{}°$

What do you notice?

Power check

How do you feel about your work in this unit?

Power puzzle

Use a ruler, protractor and sharp pencil to draw the star.

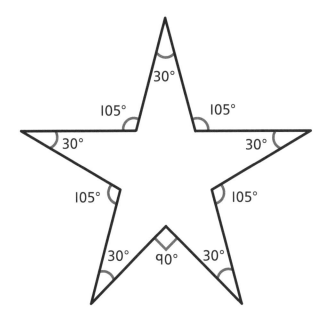

Decide how long to make each side of the star so that it can fit in the space below.

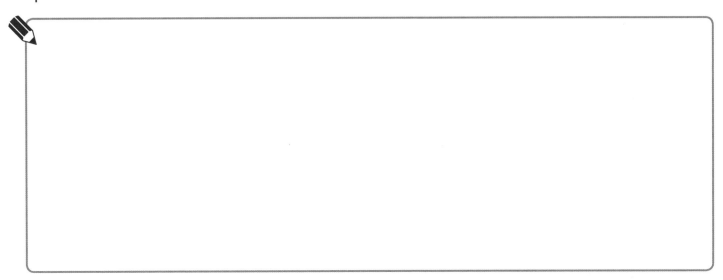

Make your own design of a geometric shape and label the angles. Challenge a partner to copy your design exactly.

Recognising and drawing parallel lines

1 There are two pairs of parallel lines in each diagram. Label the pairs of parallel lines with the signs < and <<.

23.06.22

a)

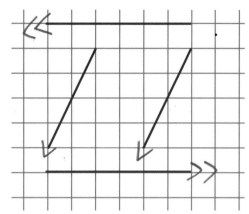

c)

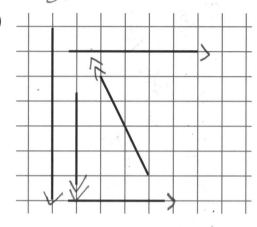

b)

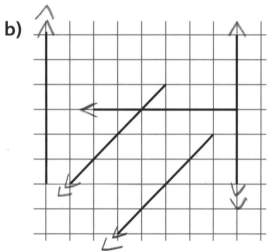

d)

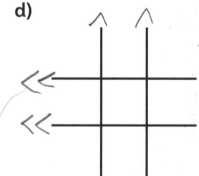

2 Mark the parallel lines on these shapes.

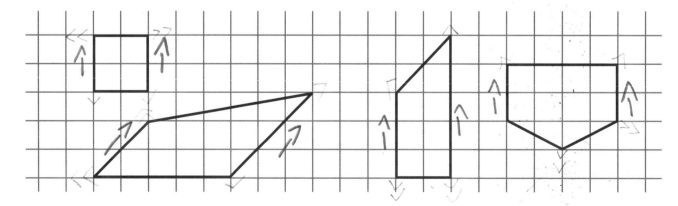

3 Draw two lines parallel to AB, two lines parallel to CD and two lines parallel to EF. The lines do not have to be the same length.

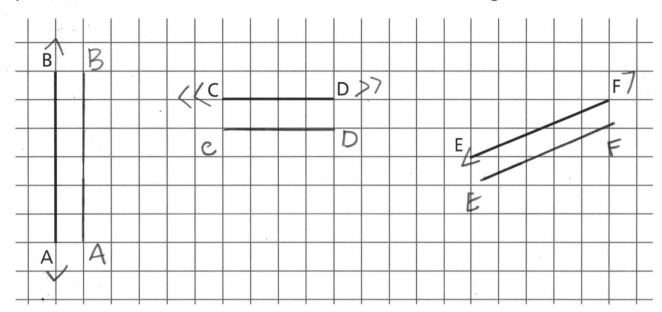

4 Complete the sentences about this shape, using the letters shown.

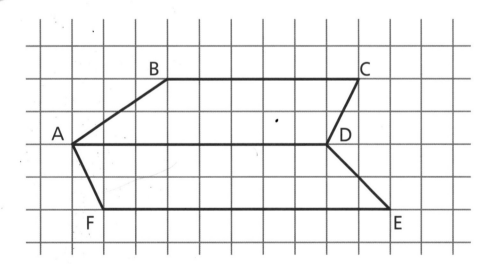

FE is parallel to ___B___ and ___C___ .

BF would be parallel to _CD_ .

Draw the line EC. Is it parallel to any lines in the shape?

_____

79

5 **a)** Mark the parallel lines on this shape.

BE is parallel to ___CD___ and _____ .

b) Complete the sentences.

CA is parallel to _____ .

BC is parallel to _____ and _____ .

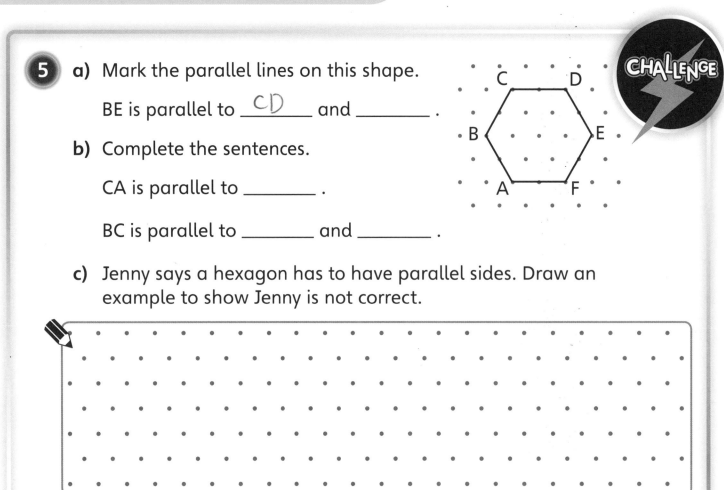

c) Jenny says a hexagon has to have parallel sides. Draw an example to show Jenny is not correct.

Reflect

Draw a shape with two pairs of parallel lines and mark them correctly. Explain how you made sure your lines are parallel.

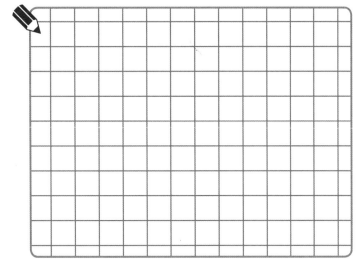

Recognising and drawing perpendicular lines

27.06.22

1 Mark the right angles where the perpendicular lines meet.

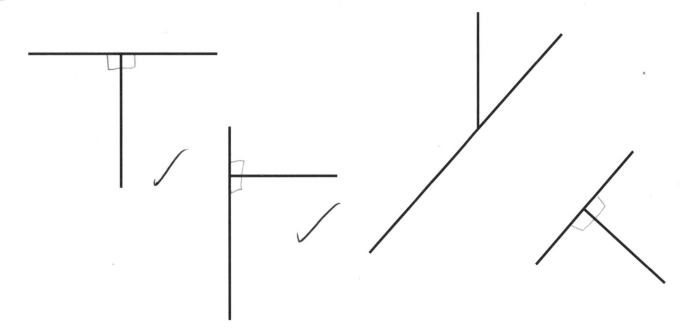

2 Draw a perpendicular line to each line below.

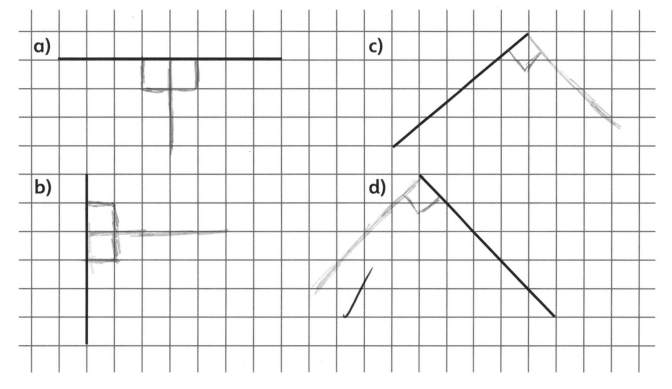

a)

b)

c)

d)

3 Mark any perpendicular lines in the shapes below.

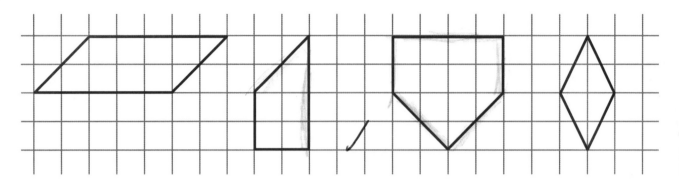

4 True or false? Circle the correct answer.
Explain your answers.

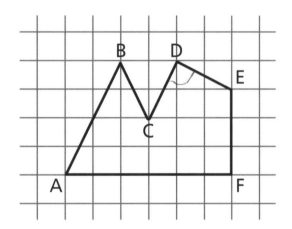

a) AB is perpendicular to BC.

True / False

Because it is not a right angle ✓

b) DE is perpendicular to EF.

True / False

there is not a right angle.

c) There is one line perpendicular to AF.

True / False

There is a right angle.

d) There are no lines perpendicular to DE.

True / False

It is false because there is a right angle. ✓

5 Draw a quadrilateral that matches one of the descriptions below.

- AB is perpendicular to BC.

- AD is perpendicular to CD.

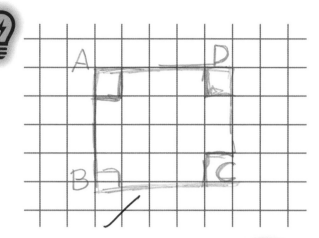

6 Draw two more lines to complete each rectangle below.

CHALLENGE

Reflect

Explain the difference between parallel and perpendicular.

parallel are lines that don't meet and perpendicular are lines that do on accout of a right angle.

Reasoning about parallel and perpendicular lines

28.06.22

1 **a)** Measure the angles below.

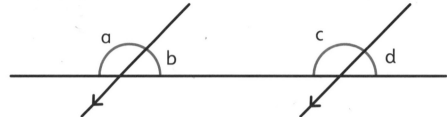

Angle a = 130 °

Angle b = 50 °

Angle c = 130 °/130

Angle d = 50 °

b) Explain what you notice about the lines.

The two diagonal lines are ___Parralell___ .

They both cross the horizontal line at angles of 130 ° and 50 °.

2 Draw a line that crosses both the parallel lines below. Measure the angles and explain what you notice.

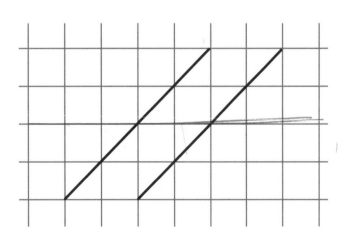

They are both paralell

45°

3 The diagonals of quadrilaterals have been drawn below. Name each quadrilateral.

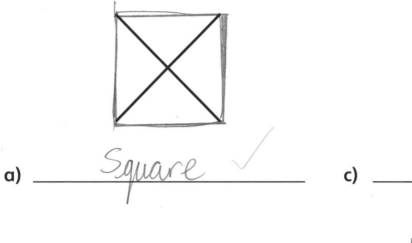

a) ___Square___ ✓

c) ___Kite___ ✓

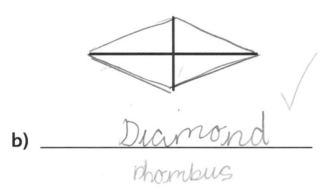

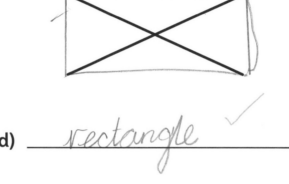

b) ___Diamond___ ✓
rhombus

d) ___rectangle___ ✓

4 Do you think the diagonals of these quadrilaterals will cross at right angles? Draw the diagonals and measure and mark the angles.

a)
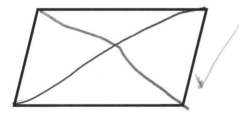

c)
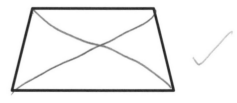

b)

d)
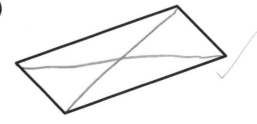

85

5 Join the dots to draw one parallel and one perpendicular line to each given line below.

CHALLENGE

Reflect

Explain how to fold a piece of paper so the folds make perpendicular lines.

Fold it into two lines.

Regular and irregular polygons 29.06.22

1 Draw a line to match each shape with the correct description. Then circle the regular shape.

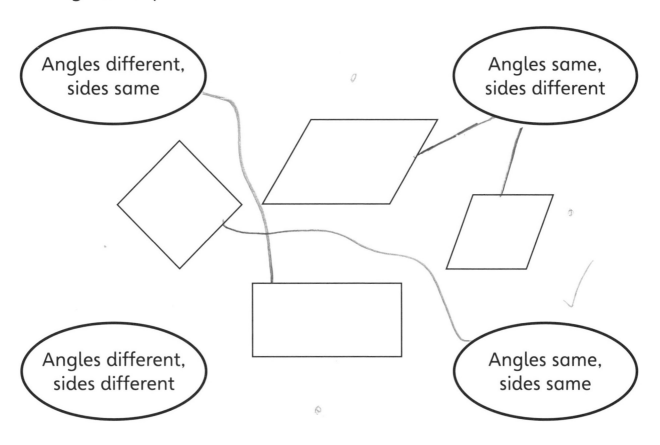

2 Look at the triangles below. Write irregular or regular for each one.

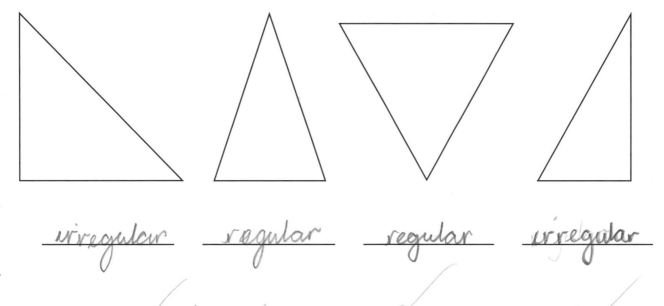

irregular   regular   regular   irregular

87

3 Explain the mistake Richard has made.

I have made a regular hexagon, because all of the angles are the same.

Richard

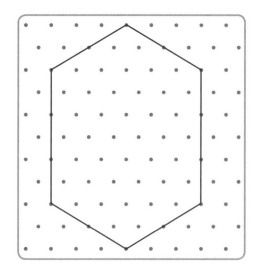

This is not a regular hexagon because _all angles have to_ _be the same for it to be_ _regular._

4 The shapes below are parts of a jigsaw puzzle.

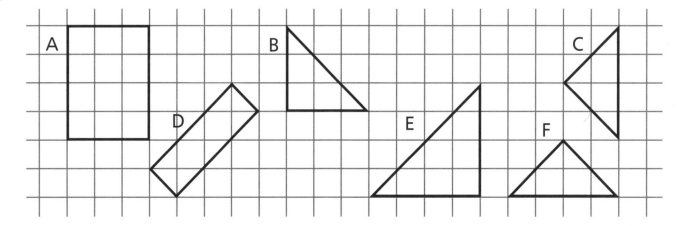

a) Which two shapes will join to make a regular shape?

___F___ and ___C___

b) Which three shapes will join to make a regular shape?

___B___ , ___C___ and ___B___

5 Draw copies of this triangle and join them together.

a) Make one regular shape and one irregular shape using six copies of the triangle for each shape.

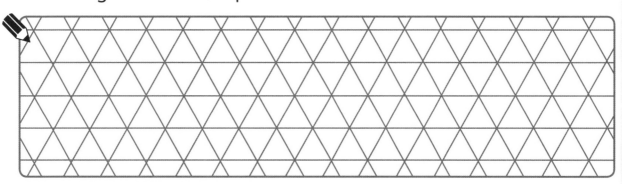

b) Make one regular and one irregular shape using four copies of the triangle for each shape.

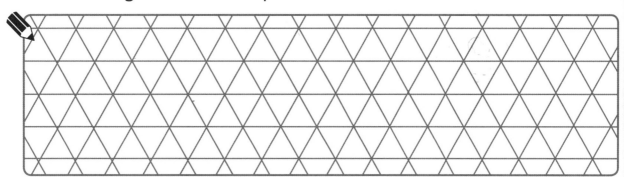

Reflect

Explain the different ways you can tell that a shape is irregular.

A shape is irregular if _____

_____

_____ .

Reasoning about 3D shapes 30.06.22

1 Draw the face of the cube that each person sees.

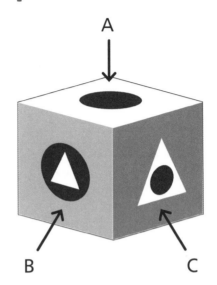

a) Person A sees:

b) Person B sees:

c) Person C sees:

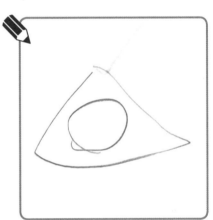

2 Circle the possible views of each cuboid.

a)

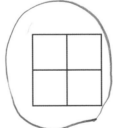

b)

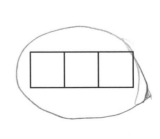
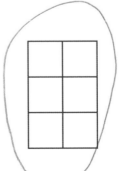
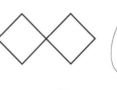
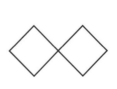
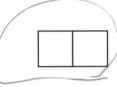
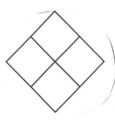

3 Three children look at the same 3D shape from different positions.

Isla sees a square, Aki sees a triangle and Jamilla sees a triangle.

Which shape could they be looking at?

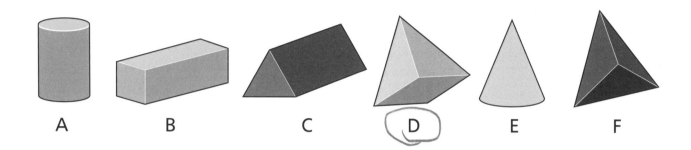

| A | B | C | D | E | F |

They could be looking at shape __D__ .

4 Draw what you would see from each different viewpoint.

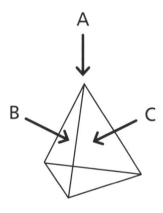

a) Person A sees:

b) Person B sees:

c) Person C sees:

5 Draw what you would see if you had a top view of these shapes.

CHALLENGE

a) b) c) d)

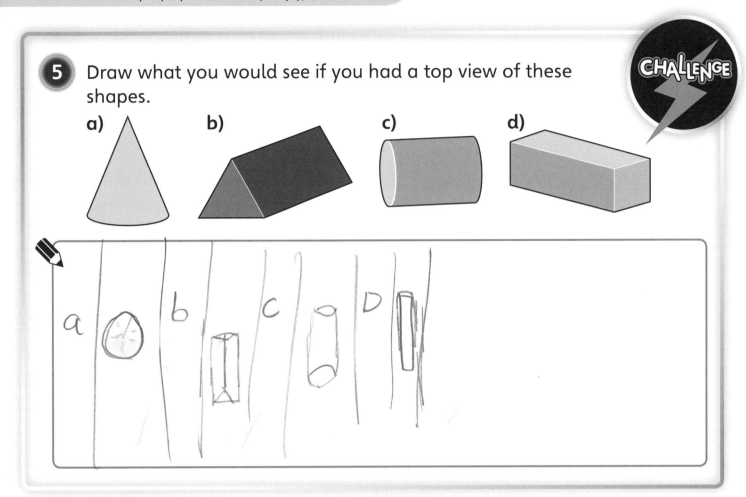

Reflect

Draw three different views of a triangular prism.

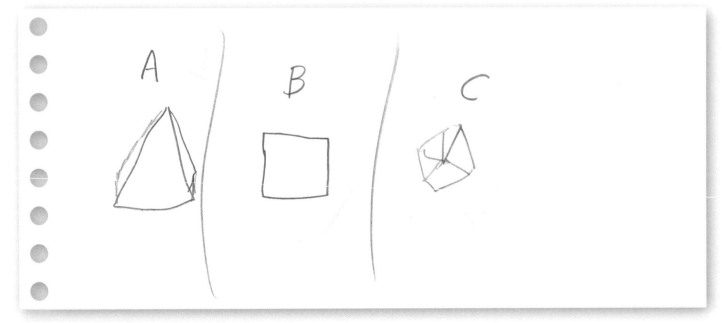

End of unit check

My journal

1 Draw different parallel lines and perpendicular lines on the two grids below. Use diagrams and words to explain your different methods.

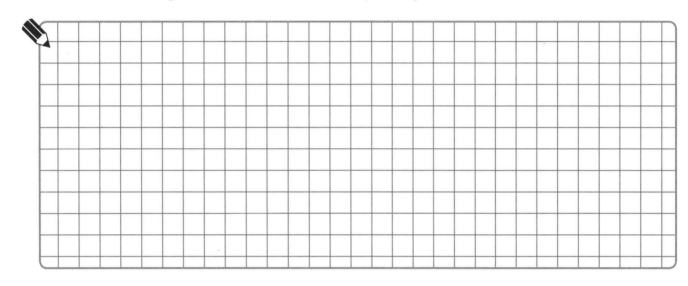

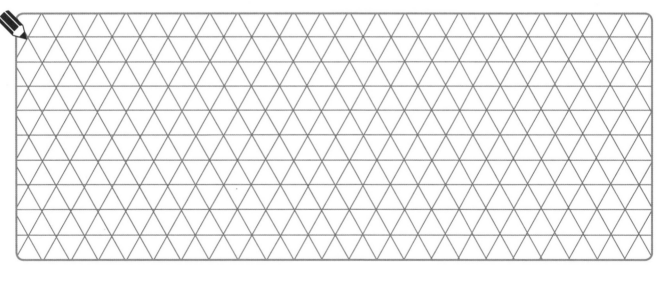

_____

_____

_____

2 Draw three different hexagons. Label all the perpendicular and parallel lines.

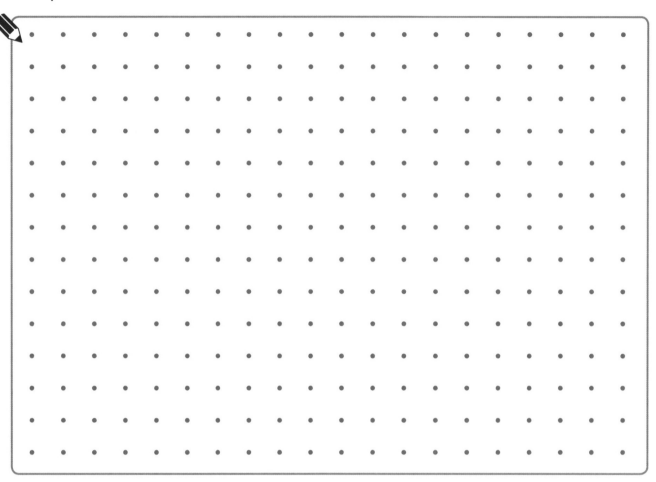

Are there any perpendicular lines that do not meet each other?

Label the vertices A–F and use this to describe any perpendicular lines.

_____

_____

_____

Power check

How do you feel about your work in this unit?

Power puzzle

Investigate how to cut a perfect square from a rectangular piece of paper.

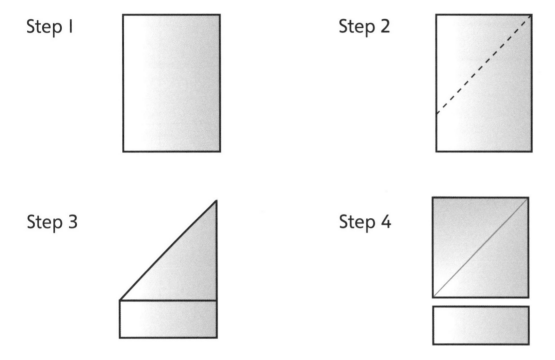

Step 1

Step 2

Step 3

Step 4

Now, take the leftover strip and fold a square from that.

Keep going with any leftover pieces and cut smaller and smaller squares.

For each square you make, measure the angles and the sides to check how accurate your squares are.

Investigate how to fold different irregular quadrilaterals from a rectangular sheet of paper.

Reflection

1 Reflect each shape in the mirror line.

a)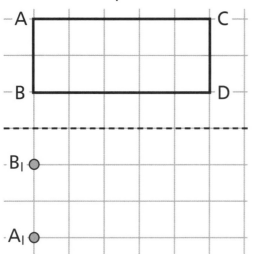

b)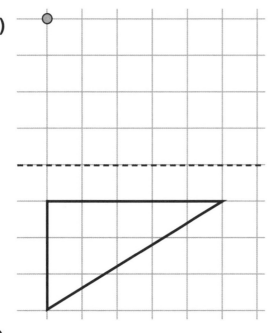

c)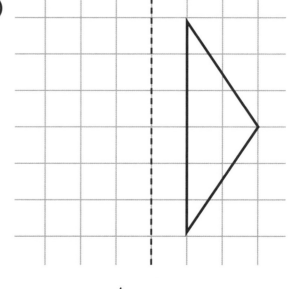

d)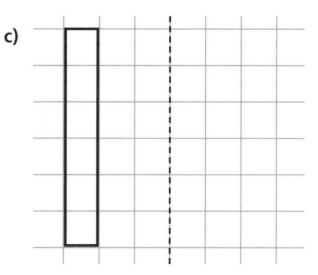

e)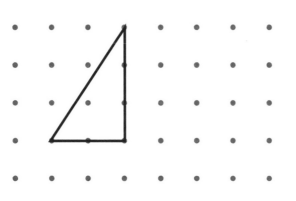

2 Predict what the reflected numbers will look like. Then check by drawing each reflection.

a) I predict that the reflected shape will look like _____

_____ .

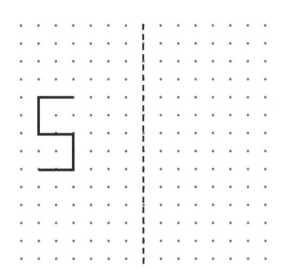

b) I predict that the reflected shape will look like _____

_____ .

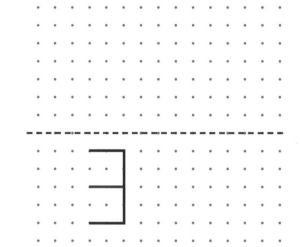

3 Draw a mirror line in the correct position between each pair of shapes.

a)

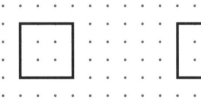

b)

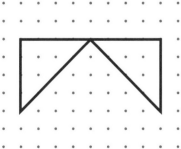

c)

d)

4 Draw each reflection.

CHALLENGE

a)

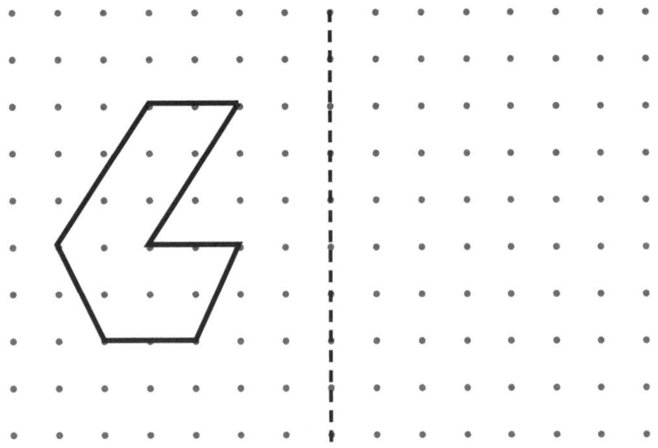

b)

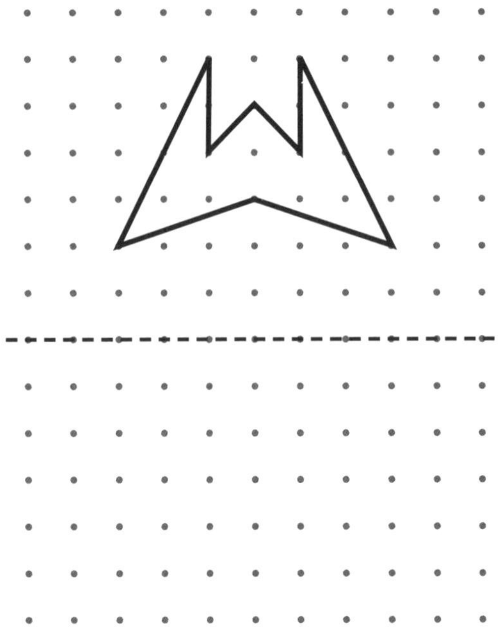

Reflect

Explain what will happen to the arrow when it is reflected in the mirror line.

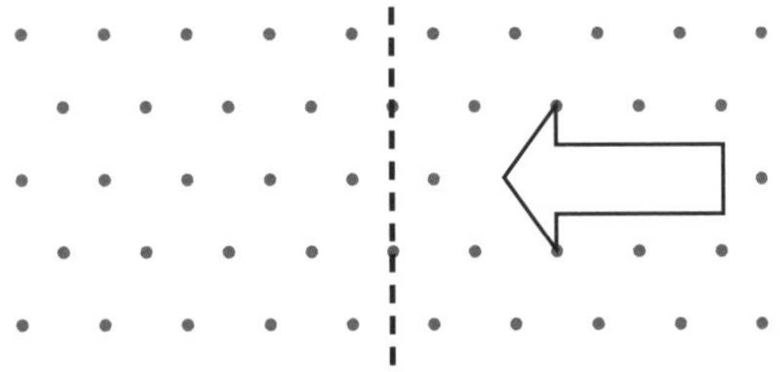

Reflection with coordinates

1 The points A to F are reflected in the mirror line.

Write the coordinates of each point and its reflected point.

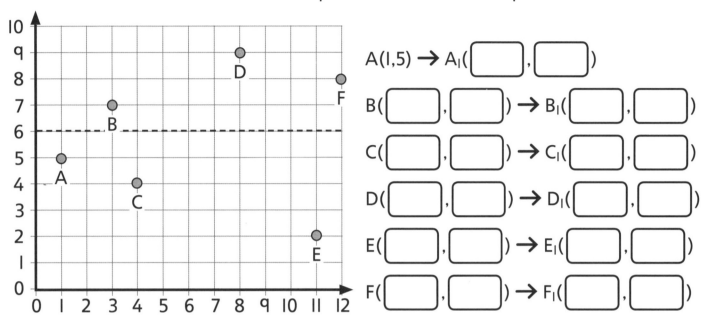

$A(1,5) \rightarrow A_1(\boxed{},\boxed{})$

$B(\boxed{},\boxed{}) \rightarrow B_1(\boxed{},\boxed{})$

$C(\boxed{},\boxed{}) \rightarrow C_1(\boxed{},\boxed{})$

$D(\boxed{},\boxed{}) \rightarrow D_1(\boxed{},\boxed{})$

$E(\boxed{},\boxed{}) \rightarrow E_1(\boxed{},\boxed{})$

$F(\boxed{},\boxed{}) \rightarrow F_1(\boxed{},\boxed{})$

2 **a)** A rectangle has vertices P(5,1), Q(7,1), R(5,4) and S(7,4).

Draw the rectangle and reflect it in the mirror line.

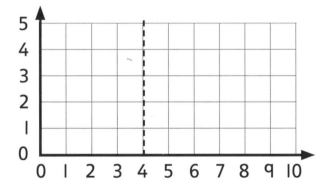

b) Write the coordinates of the reflected vertices.

$P_1(\boxed{},\boxed{})$

$Q_1(\boxed{},\boxed{})$

$R_1(\boxed{},\boxed{})$

$S_1(\boxed{},\boxed{})$

3 Write the coordinates of the reflections of the points A, B and C.

A₁([ ] , [ ])

B₁([ ] , [ ])

C₁([ ] , [ ])

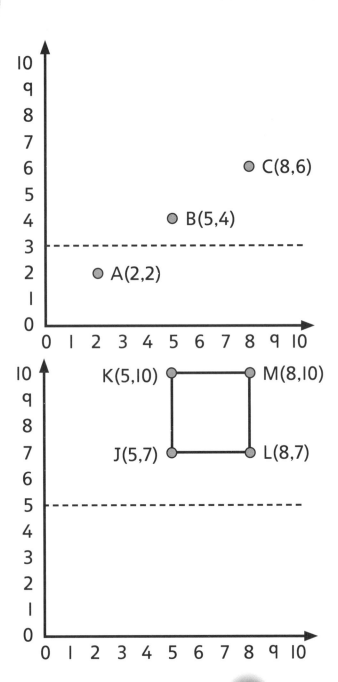

4 Write the coordinates of the reflected square.

J₁([ ] , [ ])

K₁([ ] , [ ])

L₁([ ] , [ ])

M₁([ ] , [ ])

5 The triangle is reflected in the mirror line. Calculate the new coordinates and draw the reflection as accurately as possible.

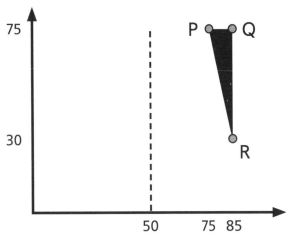

P₁([ ] , [ ])

Q₁([ ] , [ ])

R₁([ ] , [ ])

100

6 The square is reflected in the mirror line. Put one tick in each row of the table to show the correct position of each coordinate.

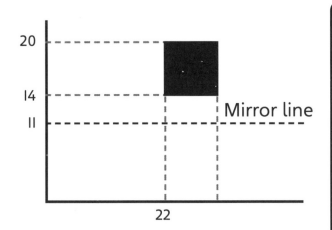

Point	Inside original square	Inside reflected square	Outside both squares
(23,21)			
(25,5)			
(29,5)			
(27,17)			
(20,7)			
(10,10)			

Reflect

Describe how you can use coordinates to calculate the reflection of a point.

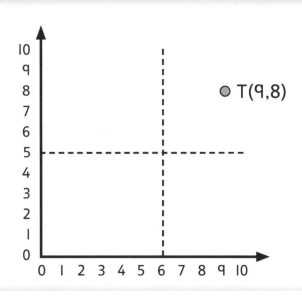

_____

_____

_____

Translation

1 Complete the translations.

a) 4 right

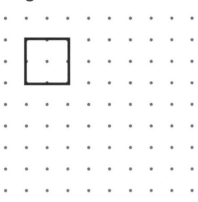

c) 4 left, 3 down

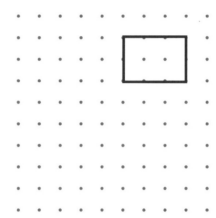

b) 5 down

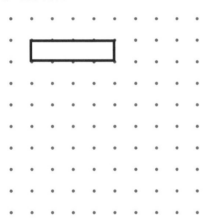

d) 6 right, 4 up

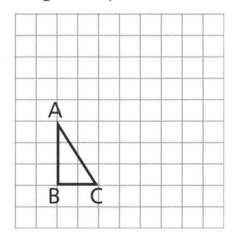

2 Describe the translation A to B.

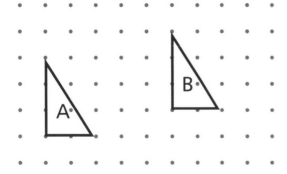

☐ right, ☐ _____

3 A rectangle has been translated 3 right, 5 up.
Draw the rectangle in its original position.

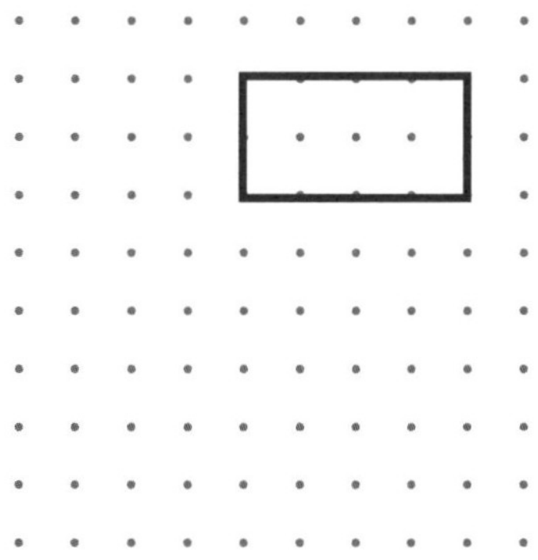

4 Look at the diagram.

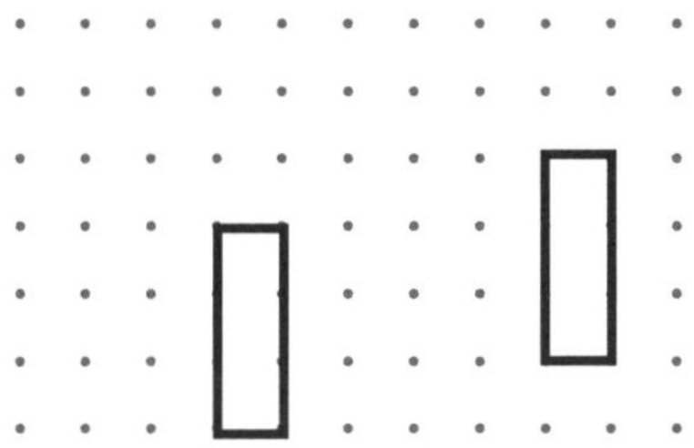

I think this was reflected in a mirror line.

Aki

No – it was translated.

Isla

Who is correct? Explain your answer fully.

_____

_____

5 Describe the translations of the grey triangles required to turn these shapes into rectangles.

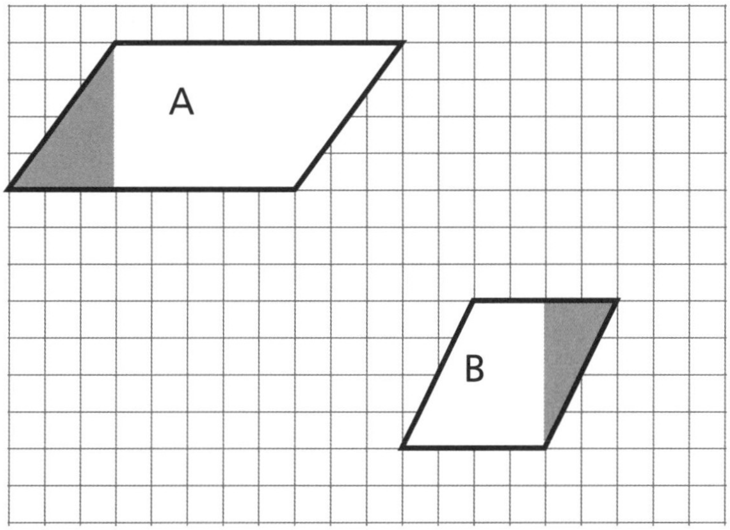

A

B

A: _____

_____

B: _____

_____

103

6 Describe the translations required to move the parts of the square to make the rocket shape.

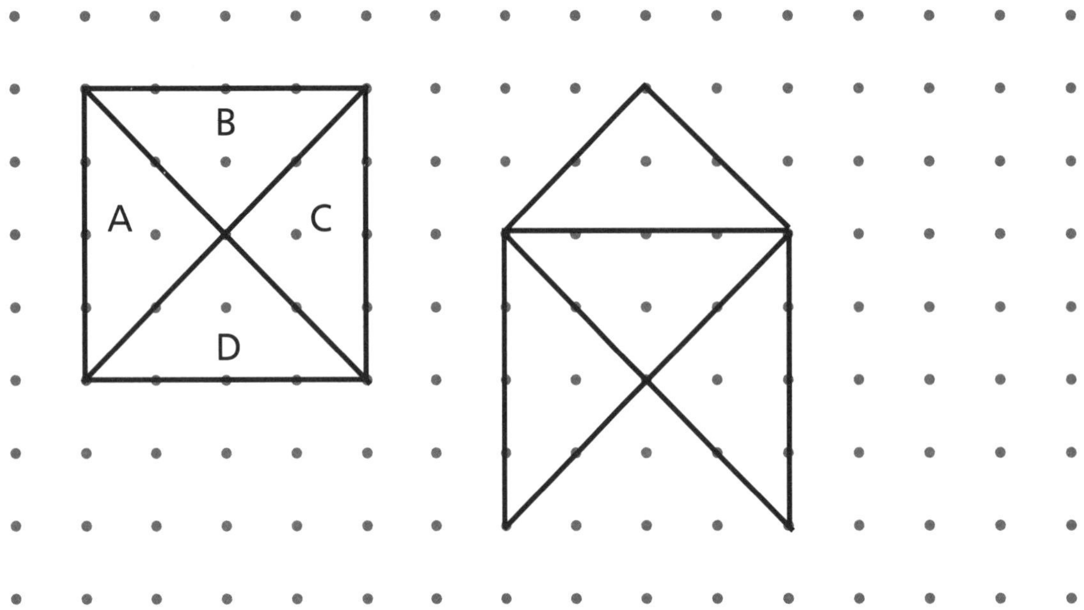

CHALLENGE

_____

_____

_____

_____

Reflect

A shape is translated 5 right and 4 down. Describe the translation that will return it to the original position.

_____

_____

_____

Translation with coordinates

1 The grid shows the starting position of points A, B and C.

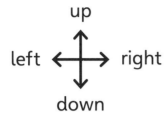

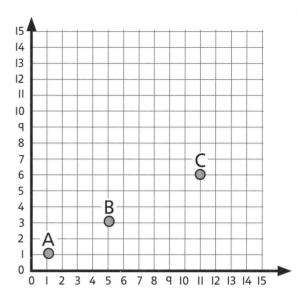

a) Perform the following translations in order and complete the table.

Translation	Position of Point A	Position of Point B	Position of Point C
Starting position	(1,1)	(5,3)	(11,6)
3 right	(4,1)		
4 left	(0,1)		
8 up			
2 down			
5 right, 4 down			
Ending position	(4,10)		

b) Write the translation from the starting position to the ending position.

Translation: _____

105

2 The rectangle is translated 20 right and 10 up. Write the coordinates of each vertex and draw the rectangle in its new position as accurately as you can.

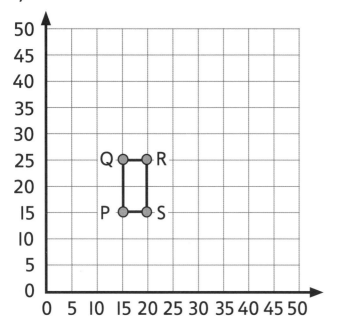

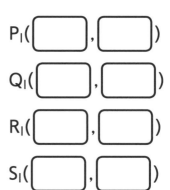

$P_1($ ☐ , ☐ $)$

$Q_1($ ☐ , ☐ $)$

$R_1($ ☐ , ☐ $)$

$S_1($ ☐ , ☐ $)$

 3 A triangle has vertices at (4,4), (10,5) and (11,10). After a translation, one vertex is at (10,6).

What translation could have been made? What are the coordinates of the other vertices?

Find more than one solution, and write the coordinates for all three vertices.

Solution 1	**Solution 2**	**Solution 3**
Translation:	Translation:	Translation:
☐ ——— ,	☐ ——— ,	☐ ——— ,
☐ ———	☐ ———	☐ ———
Vertices are:	Vertices are:	Vertices are:
(10,6)	(10,6)	(10,6)
(☐ , ☐)	(☐ , ☐)	(☐ , ☐)
(☐ , ☐)	(☐ , ☐)	(☐ , ☐)

106

4 Triangle A is translated and then reflected in the mirror line to form triangle B. Triangle B has vertices (14,25), (14,20) and (7,20).

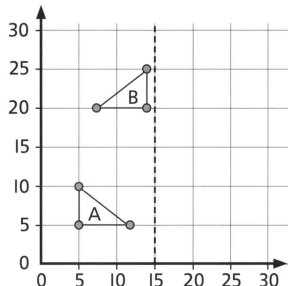

Work out what the translation is.

_____

_____

_____

Reflect

Which two methods could you use to translate this shape on a coodinate grid?

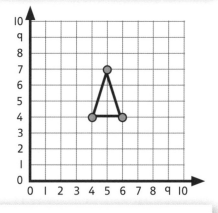

○ _____

○ _____

○ _____

End of unit check

My journal

1. This parallelogram has been reflected in the mirror line.

   What are the coordinates of the missing points A to E?

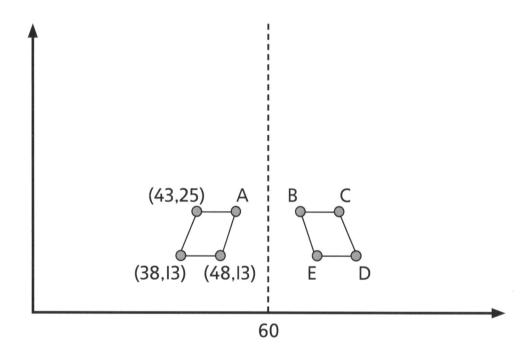

A([ ] , [ ])

B([ ] , [ ])

C([ ] , [ ])

D([ ] , [ ])

E([ ] , [ ])

2 The triangle is reflected twice. Draw the two mirror lines.

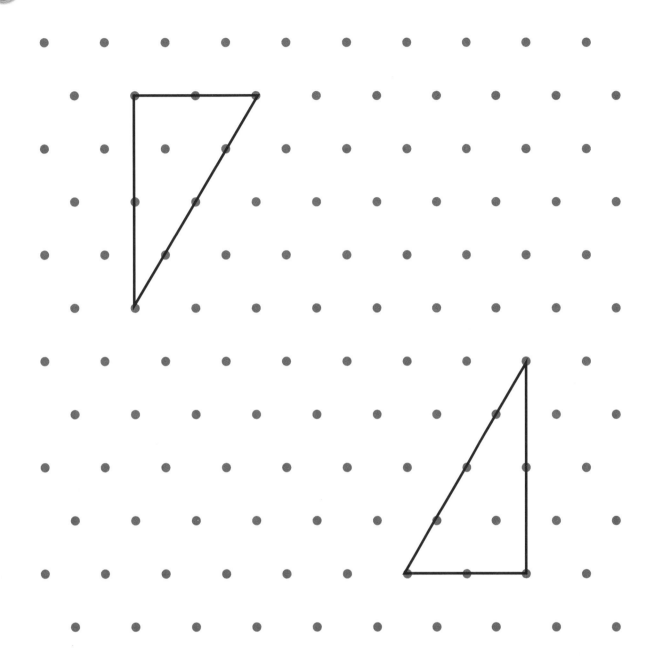

Power check

How do you feel about your work in this unit?

Power puzzle

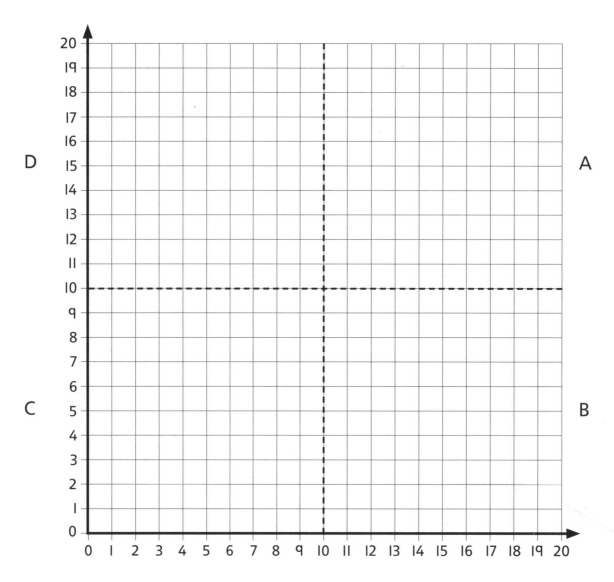

Draw a design in section A.

Reflect it in the mirror lines so you have four copies of your design.

What do you notice about the different shapes?

Try including diagonal lines, or using half-squares to make a complex symmetric pattern.

Metric units ❶

4.07.22

❶ This table shows distances between different places.

From	To	Distance
Swansea	Mumbles	7·9 km
London	Birmingham	162,000 m
Glasgow	Edinburgh	67,100 m
Manchester	Liverpool	50 km
Lynton	Lynmouth	1,300 m

a) Convert the distance from London ⟶ Birmingham into kilometres.

HTh	TTh	Th	H	T	O
1	6	2	0	0	0

To convert metres into kilometres, divide by [1000].

162,000 m ⊘ [1000] = [162]

London ⟶ Birmingham = [162] km

b) Convert the distance from Manchester ⟶ Liverpool into metres.

HTh	TTh	Th	H	T	O

To convert kilometres into metres, ⊗ by [1000].

50 km ⊗ [1000] = [50 000]

Manchester ⟶ Liverpool = [50,000] m

c) Convert the distance from Glasgow ⟶ Edinburgh into kilometres.

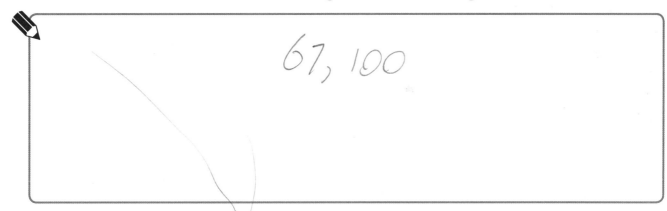

67, 100

Glasgow ⟶ Edinburgh = [   ] km

2 Which method would you use for these conversions? Write the letter in each circle.

A   Convert the length of your school hall (in metres) into kilometres.

B   Calculate the mass of a bag of potatoes (in kilograms) in grams.

C   Work out what a motorway sign showing kilometres would show as metres.

D   Change the mass of a chocolate bar (in grams) into kilograms.

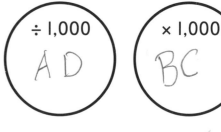

÷ 1,000

A D

× 1,000

BC

3 Complete the boxes.

a) 12 kg = $\boxed{12000}$ g

b) 8,000 g = $\boxed{8}$ kg

c) 6,500 g = $\boxed{6.5}$ kg and $\boxed{6500}$ g

d) 3·4 kg = $\boxed{3400}$ g

e) 10 kg 200 g = $\boxed{10\ 200}$ g

10 kg 200 g = $\boxed{10.2}$ kg

f) 4 kg 3,000 g = $\boxed{7000}$ g

4 kg 3,000 g = $\boxed{4.3}$ kg

4 Explain the mistake Kate has made and how to find the correct answer.

Kate

My dog has a mass of 27·5 kg. There are 1,000 grams in a kilogram, so to convert this into grams, I need to divide 27·5 by 1,000.

_____

_____

_____

5 A lorry has this dial showing the distance it has travelled.

It drives to deliver a parcel and the dial
shows a 4, a 5 and a 0.
It is not a whole number of kilometres,

How many metres could the
lorry have travelled?

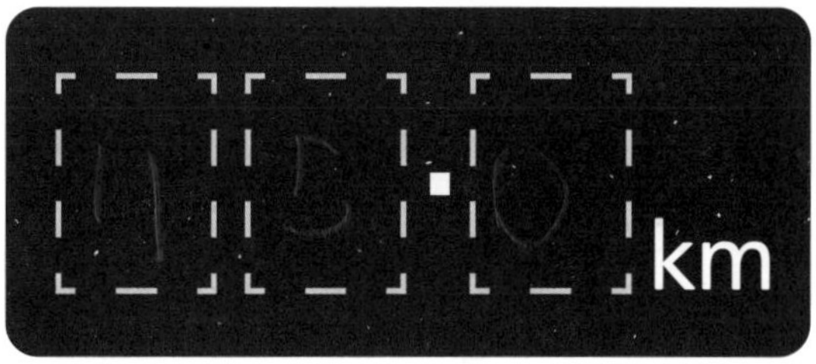

45, 000

6 Ambika has five bags of pebbles. Their masses are 18,000 g,
700 g, 5,500 g, 8,000 g and 230 g.

CHALLENGE

How many bags weigh a whole number of kilograms?
Explain your answer.

5,300

Reflect

Explain how to convert 12,500 g into kilograms.

05.07.22

Metric units ❷

1 **a)** A blade of grass is 30 mm long. How long is it in cm?

To convert mm into cm, __divide__ by [10].

30 mm ⊘ [10] = [3]

The blade of grass is [3] cm long. ✓

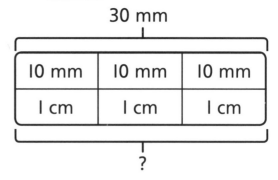

	30 mm	
10 mm	10 mm	10 mm
1 cm	1 cm	1 cm

?

b) A bottle of lemonade holds 1·2 litres. How many millilitres does it hold?

To convert __liters__ ✓ into __millitres__ , __multiply__ ✓

by [1000]. ✓

1·2 l ⊗ [1000] = [1200]

The bottle holds [1200] ml.

Th	H	T	O	•	Tth	
			1	•	2	l
				•		ml

2 **a)** Draw an arrow to show 0·35 l on the jug.

b) Draw an arrow to show 0·65 m on the ruler.

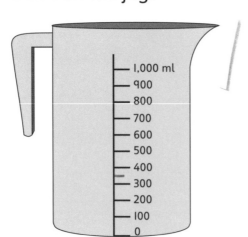

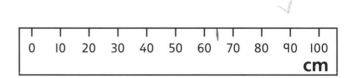

3 Draw lines to match the correct strategy with each task.

÷ 10   Convert an amount of water from millilitres into litres.

× 10   Write a length in cm as m.

÷ 1,000   Convert the height of a building (in m) into cm.

× 1,000   Change the height of a flower (in cm) into mm.

÷ 100   Convert the mass of a bag of sand (in kg) into g.

× 100   Measure the width of a stamp in mm and convert it into cm.

4 Complete the boxes.

a) 4,000 ml = [4] l ✓

b) 15 l = [1,5] ml

c) 7·2 l = [7] l and [2] ml

d) 1,600 ml = [1,6] l ✓

e) 12 l 500 ml = [51,2] ml

12 l 500 ml = [5,12] l

f) 9 l 2,500 ml = [92,5] ml

9 l 2,500 ml = [2,5] l

5 Lee measures the length of his table in metres and converts into centimetres. Mo measures the same distance in millimetres.

Explain how you know Mo is right.

My number is 10 times Lee's!

Mo

_____

_____

_____

6 The three cups below hold different amounts of liquid.

Amelia uses the cups to measure these amounts of water:
0·5 litres, 0·25 litres, 0·35 litres and 0·375 litres.

Each time she only uses three cups. Complete the table to show which cups she uses each time.

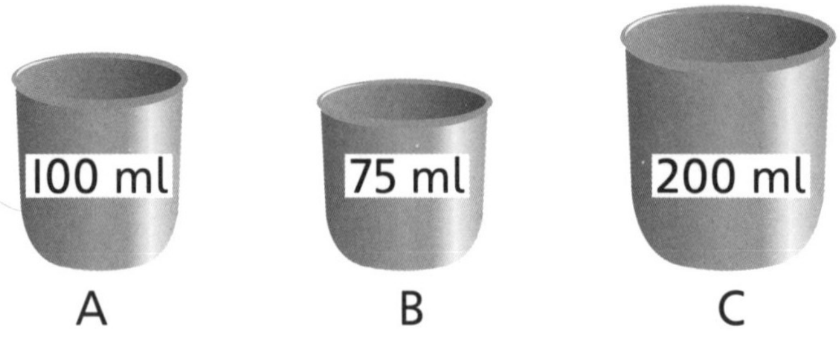

100 ml   75 ml   200 ml

A   B   C

Handwritten on left margin: 1000 6n200

First cup	Second cup	Third cup	Total
A	C	C	0·5 l
A	B	B	0·25 l
C	B	B	0·35 l
A	B	C	0·375 l

Reflect

Is Danny right or wrong? Explain your answer.

> To convert 5·6 cm into millimetres, I need to divide by 10 because 10 mm equals 1 cm.

Danny

Danny is right.

Metric units ❸

_8.07.22_

1 Convert the measurements to find the totals.

a)

7,200 ml   1 l

Th	H	T	O	•	Tth
			1	•	
				•	

7,200 ml   +   ✓1 l   ✓

= [7,200] ml + [1000] ml = [8,200] ml

b)

6·2 kg   2,000 g

Th	H	T	O	•	Tth
				•	
				•	

[6.2] kg + [2000] g ✓

= [6,200] g + [2000] g = [8,200] g ✓

c) In each of these examples, I converted the numbers by ___1000___ ✓

_____ .

1400 cm

2 A length of string is 1·4 m long. An 80 cm long piece is cut from it.

What length of string is left in centimetres? Mark your answer on the ruler.

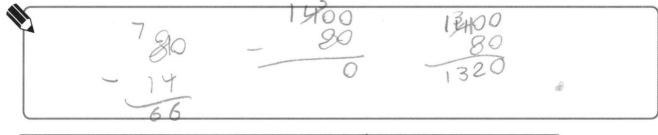

3
1400
  80
_____
   0

1400
  80
_____
1320

7
80
- 14
____
66

| 0 | 10 | 20 | 30 | 40 | 50 | 60 | 70 | 80 | 90 | 100 |

cm

117

3 Show how you can find each answer using two different units.

a) 800 g + $\frac{1}{2}$ kg   *500*

   = 800 g + [500] g

   = [1300] g

   800 g + $\frac{1}{2}$ kg ✓

   = [0.8] kg + [0.5] kg

   = [1.3] kg ✓

b) 10·5 cm – 62 mm   *1 0.5* *6.2*

   = 10·5 cm – [6.2] cm

   = [4.3] cm ✓

   10·5 cm – 62 mm

   = [6.2] mm – 62 mm

   = [62] mm

4 Put these shopping bags in order from lightest to heaviest.

A   B   C   D

Lightest ___C___ , ___D___ , ___A___ , ___B___ Heaviest

5 Richard makes some orange squash by mixing $\frac{1}{10}$ litre of orange juice with 1 litre of water.

He pours 300 ml of squash into a glass.

CHALLENGE

a) How many millilitres of squash does he have left? Show your working.

> This information uses different units! I think I am going to need to convert.

Richard has [ ] ml of squash left.

b) Richard divides the rest of the squash into 4 glasses equally. How much squash is in each glass?

Each glass has [ ] ml of squash.

Reflect

How would you write the total of 250 m and 0·6 km in metres?

Metric units ④

1 Complete the bar models to help show each conversion.

a) [10] mm = 1 cm

To convert from mm to cm, divide by [10].

1 cm	
	[10] mm

b) [100] cm = 1 m

[1000] m = 1 km

[100] × [1000] = [100,000]

1 m	
	[10] km

To convert from cm to km, ÷ by [100,000].

To convert from km to cm, ⊗ by [1,001,000].

[1] km	
[1000] m	

2 a) The tail of a mouse is 142 mm.
How many centimetres is this?

The mouse's tail is [ ] cm long.

H	T	O	•	Tth
			•	
			•	

Draw the mouse's tail to the correct length.

142 ÷ 10 = 14.2 cm

b) Andy has a pedometer.
It says he has walked 40,000 cm.

Convert this into more suitable units.

40,000 cm = [400] m = [0.4] km

TTh	Th	H	T	O	•	Tth
4	0	0	0	0	•	
		4	0	0	•	
					•	

3 Year 5 are having a sunflower growing competition. Here are their results:

Name	Lexi	Ebo	Max	Reena
Height of sunflower	1·3 m	$1\frac{1}{4}$ m	123 cm	1,252 mm

Write the children's names in order from tallest to shortest sunflower.

_____1.252 m_____ ___1.25 m_____ _____1.23 m_____ _____1.3 m_____

4 The length of a piece of ribbon is 2 m. It has a width of 3 cm.

3 cm

2 m = 200 cm

a) Danny says the perimeter is 10 cm. What mistake has he made?

_____

_____

b) Work out the correct perimeter.

The perimeter is ☐ cm = ☐ m.

121

5 **a)** The length of the smallest dog in the world is 15·2 cm.
Mark its length on this ruler.

CHALLENGE

| 0 | 10 | 20 | 30 | 40 | 50 | 60 | 70 | 80 | 90 | 100 | 110 | 120 | 130 | 140 | 150 | 160 | 170 | 180 | 190 | 200 |

mm

b) The longest straw used to drink cola in the world is 75·82 m!
How many centimetres will the cola need to travel before you
can taste it?

The cola will travel ☐ cm.

c) The narrowest street in the world is 310 mm wide. Would you be
able to walk down it? Explain your answer.

_____

_____

Reflect

Complete the sentences in as many ways as you can.

There are 10 _____ in ☐ _____ .

There are 100 _____ in ☐ _____ .

There are 1,000 _____ in ☐ _____ .

Imperial units of length

11.07.22

1 **a)** Draw a circle around each imperial unit.

10 inch pizza

Leeds
50 kilometres

25 metres

Park
100 yards

20 centimetres

6 feet 2 inches

15 millimetre screws

b) Complete each sentence with one of the cards.

I inch is approximately ___2 ½ cm___ .

I foot is equal to ___12 inches___ .

I yard is equal to ___3 feet___ .

3 feet

2 ½ cm

12 inches

2 Use your answers from I b) to help you answer this question.

This snake is 4 feet long.

How many inches long is the snake?

4 feet

$\boxed{4} \times \boxed{12} = \boxed{48}$

The snake is $\boxed{48}$ inches long.

I foot			
12 inches			

3 The ruler below shows inches and centimetres but is incomplete.

Add the missing labels.

0	1	2	3	4	5	6	7	8	9
inches
cm
0	2·5	5	7·5	1	3.5	6	8.5	11	13.5

4 Circle the correct measurement.

a) Which is taller: a 48 inch chimpanzee or a ⟨3 ½ foot baboon?⟩
Show your working.

$$3 \times 12 = 36$$
$$12 \times 5 = 60$$
$$> + = 96 \text{ inch}$$

b) Which is longer? A ~~6 yard~~ pond or a ⟨21 foot patio?⟩ Show your working.
18 feet

$$1 \text{ yard} = 3 \text{ feet} \qquad 18 \text{ feet} < 21 \text{ feet}$$
$$6 \times 3 = 18$$

5 The sat nav in Mr Lopez's car is set to imperial measurements.

It says, 'Turn left in 20 yards. Continue for 100 yards.'

Convert these distances into metres. Show your working.

> I yard is about the same as 90 cm.

20 yards is about ☐ m. 100 yards is about ☐ m.

6 The width of this television screen is 55 inches.
Complete the bar model and the conversions.

← 55 inches →

55 inches

12 inches	12 inches	12 inches	12 inches	7 in
I foot				

= [ ] ft [ ] in

= [ ] yd [ ] ft [ ] in

7 **a)** Jamie says that a typical human is about 2 feet tall.
What mistake might she have made?

CHALLENGE

_____

_____

b) How tall are you in centimetres? How about in feet and inches?

_____

_____

Reflect

What have you learnt about imperial units for length in this lesson? Write down
as many things as you can.

- _____
- _____
- _____

Imperial units of mass

I pound (I lb) is the same as I6 ounces (I6 oz).

1 Complete the number line. Use it to work out each conversion.

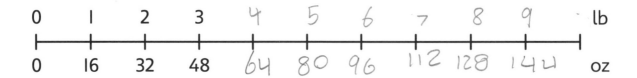

0	I	2	3	4	5	6	7	8	9	lb

0	16	32	48	64	80	96	112	128	144	oz

a) 3 lb = $\boxed{48}$ oz

b) $\boxed{7}$ lb = II2 oz

c) 5 lb = $\boxed{80}$ oz

d) 8 lb 2 oz = $\boxed{130}$ oz

e) $\boxed{}$ lb $\boxed{}$ oz = 5I oz

f) $\frac{1}{2}$ lb = $\boxed{}$ oz

g) $\frac{1}{4}$ lb = $\boxed{}$ oz

h) 4·5 lb = $\boxed{}$ oz

2 a) What is the mass of the box of oranges in pounds?

The box of oranges has a mass of $\boxed{17}$ lb. pounds

b) How many ounces is this equal to?

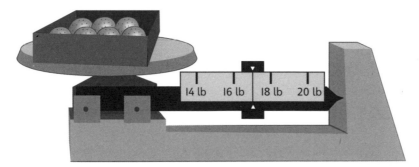

$\boxed{16}$ lb = $\boxed{23}$ oz

3 I kg is about the same as 2·2 lb.

Max says that his cat has a mass of about 5 kg.

Complete the bar model to show whether Max is correct.

II lb

5 kg

I kg				
2·2 lb				

| 110 | lb

4 Help Richard solve the problem. Explain your answer.

I pound is about 450 g. I wonder how you can find $3\frac{1}{2}$ lbs in kilograms?

Richard

_____

_____

5 Crack the code!

a) Colour the three measurements that are approximately equal to I0 lb.

	S = 4·5 g	O = 4·5 kg	R = I·6 oz
	I = 450 g	A = 450 kg	N = I60 oz
	T = 4,500 g	E = 4,500 kg	P = I6 oz

b) Rearrange the three letters you coloured in to spell a different imperial unit (equal to 2,240 lb).

The imperial unit is _____ .

6 A giant octopus has a mass of about 7 stone and 2 lb.

CHALLENGE

a) What is its mass in pounds?

The giant octopus has a mass of ☐ lb.

> I stone (st) = 14 lb
>
> I kg = 2·2 lb

b) What is its mass in kilograms?

> I can work out 10 lb and use this to help me work out my answer.

The giant octopus has a mass of ☐ kg.

Reflect

A small dog has a mass of 14 lb. Describe how you could calculate this mass in metric units.

_____

_____

_____

Imperial units of capacity 13.07.22

1 I pint is approximately equal to 570 ml.

Add 570 each time and complete the bar model.

I pt	2 pt	3 pt	4 Pt	5 Pt	6pt	7pt	8pt
570 ml	1,140 ml	1,710 ml	2,280ml	2,850ml	3,429ml	3990n	4560ml

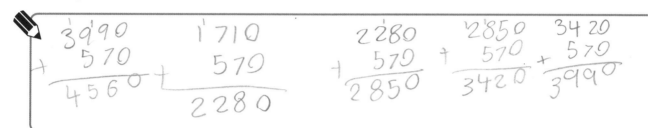

```
  3990        1710        2280      2850    34 20
+  570            570    +  570  +  570  +  570
------      + ------      ------    ------  ------
  4560    +     2280        2850    3420    3990
```

2 Use the bar model in question I to complete these measurements.

a) 5 pints = ⟨2,850⟩ ml

b) ⟨8⟩ pints = 4,560 ml

c) 3 pints = ⟨1,710⟩ ml

d) I litre 140 ml = ⟨31.5⟩ pints

e) ⟨3,420⟩ litres ⟨0⟩ ml = 6 pints

f) ⟨7⟩ pints = 3·99 litres

g) ½ pint = ⟨285⟩ millilitres

```
1.75 pints
  175
+ 140
------
  315
```

```
  285
2)51710
```

```
2 85
3,990 01000

39,900
```

3 There are 8 pints in a gallon.

Circle the measurement that is nearest to I gallon.

4 litres   4 ½ litres   5 litres

Explain your answer.

_____

_____

4 Which pond contains the most water?

Complete the number line, then mark each pond on the number line with an arrow.

75 pints

9 gallons
7 pints

A   B   C

$9 \frac{1}{2}$ gallons

```
0    1    2    3                                          gallons
├────┼────┼────┼────┼────┼────┼────┼────┼────┼────┼────┤
0    8                                                   pints
```

Pond _____ contains the most water.

5 How much milk is in this jug? Give your answer in pints and litres.

4 pints

2

0

The jug contains ☐ pints

= ☐ litres.

1 pint = approximately 570 ml

6 Three bottles of lemonade contain 200 ml each. Lexi pours them into a jug.

Mark a line on the jug where you think the lemonade will roughly be.

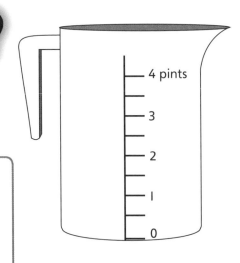

4 pints

3

2

1

0

130

7 Luis's mother wants to fill up her car with 10 gallons of fuel. At petrol station A, fuel costs £5 per gallon. Petrol station B charges £1 per litre.

CHALLENGE

a) Which petrol station is cheaper?

Petrol station _____ is cheaper.

b) How much money does Luis's mother save by going to this petrol station?

She saves £ [ ] .

Reflect

You have been asked to go to buy 2 pints of milk. It is only sold in litres. How many litres would you buy? Explain your answer.

Converting units of time   13.07.22

1 Complete the bar models to convert these times.

a) How many hours is a 310 minute rail journey?

310 minutes		
60 mins	5 hours	10mins

The rail journey is [5] hours [10] minutes.

b) How many minutes is a 195 second pop song?

195 s	
60 s	

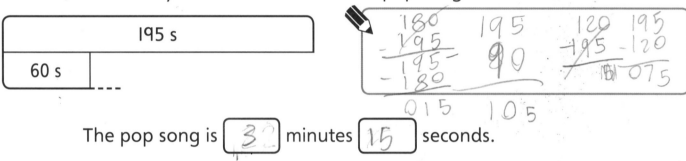

```
  180      195      120  195
- 195      -90     +195 -120
- 195                     075
- 180
  015      105
```

The pop song is [3] minutes [15] seconds.

2 The films below have different running times. Which film is longer?

Draw a bar model to help you find the answer.

KING OF THE PENGUINS

2 hours 7 minutes

Escape from PLANET Zarg

137 minutes

2 : 17

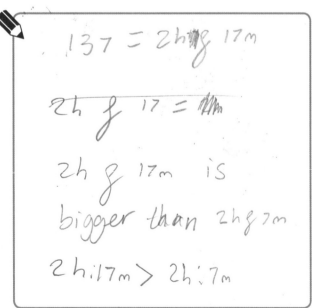

```
137 = 2h 17m

2h 17 = m

2h 17m is
bigger than 2h 7m

2h 17m > 2h 7m
```

Escape from planet Zarg is longer.

3 Is Ambika correct?
Explain your answer.

4·25 hours is 4 hours and 25 minutes.

Ambika

No because it is wrong.

4 Here are the lengths of the summer holidays for four children.

Name	Kate	Lee	Bella	Mo
Length of holidays	21 July to 2 September	40 days	5 weeks and 4 days	The whole of August plus 10 days

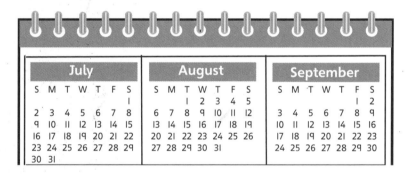

Put their names in order, from shortest holiday to longest. Show your working.

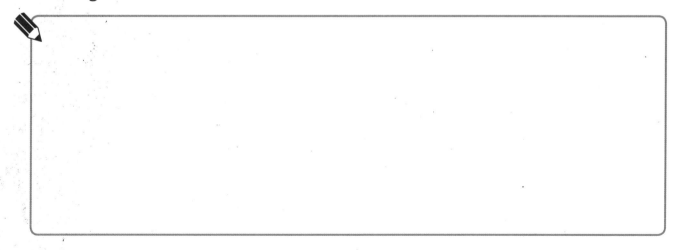

_____ _____ _____ _____

5 These function machines convert from one time into another.

This machine converts hours to minutes.

hours ⟶ ×60 ⟶ minutes

a) Complete these function machines to show what they do.

hours ⟶ ×60 ⟶ ×60 ⟶ _____

days ⟶ ×24 ⟶ ×60 ⟶ _____

days ⟶ ÷7 ⟶ _____

b) Draw a function machine to show how you would find the number of minutes in a leap year.

Reflect

Describe how you would convert 30 months into years and months.

_____

_____

_____

Timetables

14.07.22

1 Look carefully at this coach timetable.

Stop	Coach A	Coach B	Coach C	Coach D	Coach E	Coach F
Birmingham Bus Station	05:45	07:30	09:20	11:15	12:50	14:35
Gilbertstone	06:05	07:50	09:40	11:35	13:10	14:55
Birmingham Airport	06:15	08:00	09:50	11:45	13:20	15:05
Coventry Bus Station	06:40	08:25	10:15	12:10	13:45	15:30
Northampton Bus Station	07:40	09:25	11:15	13:10	14:45	16:30
Luton Airport	08:45	10:30	12:20	14:15	15:50	17:35
Hertford North Station	09:30	11:15	13:05	15:00	16:35	18:20
Stansted Airport	10:20	12:05	13:55	15:50	17:25	19:10

a) Complete the sentences.

There are ☐ 6 rows in the timetable. Each row shows a different

___Timetable___ .

There are ☐ 8 columns. Each column shows a different ___Stop___ .

The times in the timetable are ☐ 12 hour times.

b) What time does the coach that leaves Gilbertstone at five minutes past 6 arrive at Luton Airport?   It arrives at ☐ 8 : 25 .

c) What time did the ten minutes to 4 arrival at Luton Airport leave Birmingham Bus Station?   It left at ☐ 15 : 30 .

d) Complete the sentence.

At ☐ 13 : 5 Coach D arrives at Luton Airport.

Its next stop is _____ .

It takes ☐ minutes to get there and it arrives at ☐ : .

135

2 This is part of a railway timetable.

Grantham	06:31	07:23	08:16	09:32	11:27	12:25
Rauceby	–	07:46	08:40	–	–	–
Sleaford	06:57	07:51	08:45	09:58	11:53	12:50
Boston	07:25	08:18	09:12	10:26	12:19	13:15
Thorpe Culvert	07:47	–	–	10:48	–	–
Wainfleet	07:51	08:43	09:36	10:52	12:44	13:40
Havenhouse	07:55	–	–	10:56	–	–
Skegness	08:05	08:56	09:49	11:06	12:58	13:54

a) Olivia arrives at <u>Boston</u> at <u>10 o'clock</u> and catches the next train to <u>Skegness</u>. How long is she on the train for?

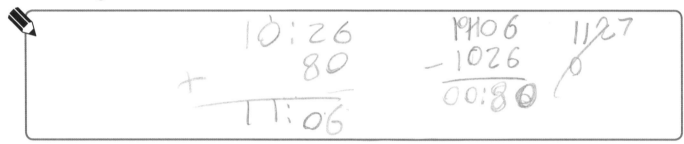

10:26
+   80
11:06

11106
−1026
00:80

11:27

She is on the train for ⬜80 minutes. ✓

b) It is <u>09:33</u>. Mo is at <u>Grantham</u> and has just missed the train! How long will he wait for the next train to Skegness?

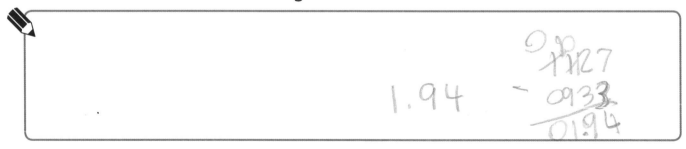

1.94

11:27
−09:33
01:94

He will wait ⬜2 hours and ⬜34 minutes.

c) A train leaves Grantham at quarter past 1 in the afternoon. It makes the same stops as the 06:31 train and takes the same time to travel between stops. Complete the final column of the timetable to show this train.

3 A school bus makes this journey from Hall Lane to Moorfield Academy.

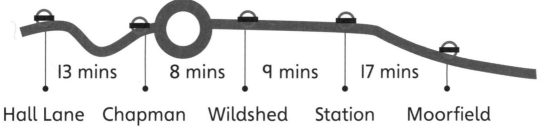

| 13 mins | 8 mins | 9 mins | 17 mins | |
| Hall Lane | Chapman Avenue | Wildshed Road | Station Road | Moorfield Academy |

Complete the timetable to include:

• a bus that leaves Hall Lane at twenty minutes to 8 in the morning

• a bus that arrives at Moorfield Academy at twenty-five minutes to 4 in the afternoon.

	Bus 1	Bus 2
Hall Lane		
Chapman Avenue		
Wildshed Road		
Station Road		
Moorfield Academy		

I am going to have to work back in time for one of these buses!

Reflect

Why do you think timetables are written using 24-hour clock times? Think about the mistakes that could happen if they were not.

Problem solving – measure

1 A bag of coins has a mass of 2·7 kg. How many grams is this?

2·7 kg is [ ] grams.

2 This ruler shows the distance that a frog has jumped.

How many metres has it jumped?

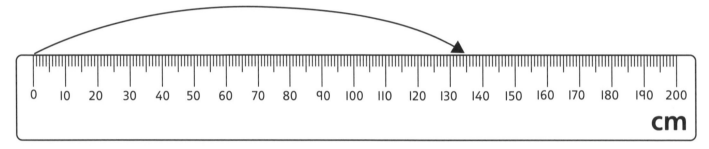

The frog has jumped [ ] metres.

3 A teacup holds 150 ml. Zac empties three teacups of water into a measuring jug.

Mark the level of the water that is now in the jug.

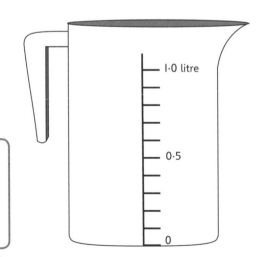

4 A box of strawberries has a mass of 1·6 kg. It is shared equally among 10 people. How many grams of strawberries do they have each?

They have ⬚ grams each.

5 Ebo's mum wants to buy 4 yards of material to make a dress.

Shop A sells material for £1·50 per yard. Shop B sells the same material for £2 per metre.

Which shop is cheaper?

I yard is approximately 90 cm.

Shop _____ is cheaper.

6 A net of 5 footballs has a mass of 2·8 kg in total.

The net itself has a mass of 800 g.

What mass does 1 football have in grams?

One football has a mass of ⬚ g.

7 These photo frames are the same distance apart on a wall. Each photo frame is 20 cm wide. The total length of wall that the frames take up is 1·25 m.

CHALLENGE

What is the length of each space between the photos?

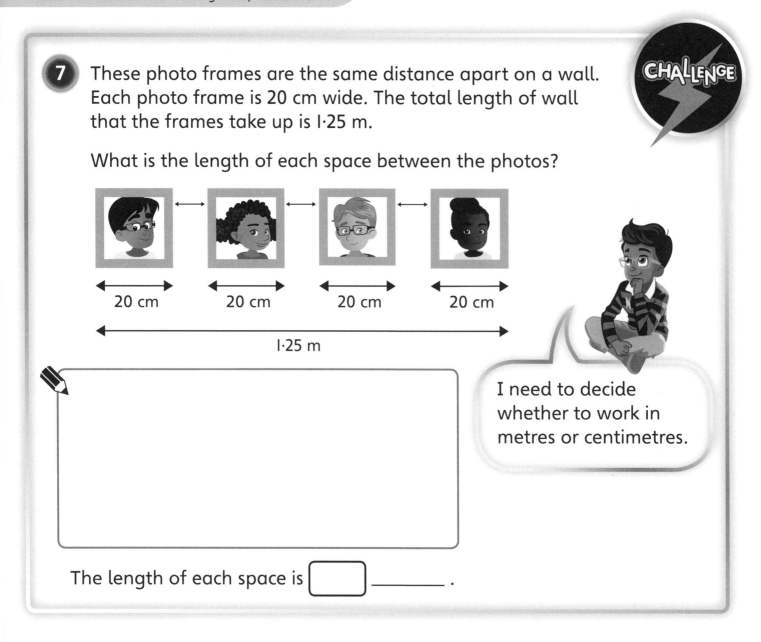

I need to decide whether to work in metres or centimetres.

The length of each space is ⬚ _____ .

Reflect

Olivia has a ball of string and a ruler that measures in inches.
She needs to cut a piece of string 1 m long. Explain how she can measure it.

End of unit check

My journal

1 Explain how you would convert these measurements.

My bottle holds 1·2 litres of water. How many millilitres is this?

Bella

a) 1·2 litres = ⬚ millilitres

I know this because _____

_____

_____ .

My train journey took 490 minutes. How many hours and minutes did it take?

Andy

b) 490 minutes = ⬚ hours ⬚ minutes

I know this because _____

_____

_____ .

How many metres are the same as 60 inches?

Danny

c) 60 inches = ⬚ metres

I know this because _____

_____

_____ .

Power check

How do you feel about your work in this unit?

Power play

Play this game of three-in-a-row with a partner. You will need: different coloured counters, a dice and this railway timetable.

START						
Greenhill	06:42	10:02	13:22	16:42	20:02	23:22
Newton	06:57	10:17	13:37	16:57	20:17	23:37
Wood End	07:18	10:38	13:58	17:18	20:38	23:58
Amington	07:27	10:47	14:07	17:27	20:47	00:07
Ellwich	07:42	11:02	14:22	17:42	21:02	00:22
Garford	08:05	11:25	14:45	18:05	21:25	00:45

Put a counter on START.

Roll a dice. Move your counter that number of squares right. Roll the dice again. Move your counter that number of squares down.

Say a fact about the square you land on. For example, if you have rolled a 3 and a 4, you could say: 'The twenty-two minutes past 1 train from Greenhill arrives at Amington at seven minutes past 2.'

If you and your partner agree this is a correct fact, leave your plastic counter on the square.

Take turns with your partner, alternating between moving to the left, right, up and down.

The winner is the first person to have three counters in a row.

Try inventing your own game where your partner has to work out the time different trains take!

What is volume?

1 What is the volume of each shape?

a)

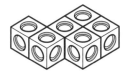

Volume = [ ]
unit cubes

c)

Volume = [ ]
unit cubes

e)

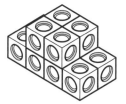

Volume = [ ]
unit cubes

b)

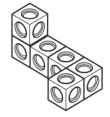

Volume = [ ]
unit cubes

d)

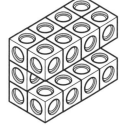

Volume = [ ]
unit cubes

f)

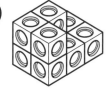

Volume = [ ]
unit cubes

2 Match the shapes to the correct volume.

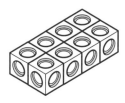   

6 unit cubes   8 unit cubes   12 unit cubes   16 unit cubes

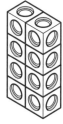 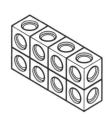 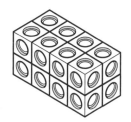 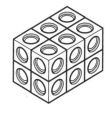

3

The volume of this 3D shape is 6 unit cubes.

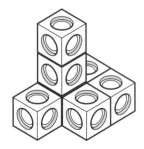

Richard

Do you think Richard is correct? Explain your answer.

_____

_____

4 What is the volume of each of the following shapes?

A   B   C

Shape	Volume
Shape A	5 unit cubes
Shape B	☐ unit cubes
Shape C	☐ _____

Explain how you got your answers.

_____

_____

5 Draw a copy of each cube on the isometric grid.

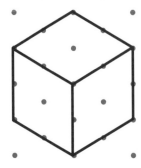

6 Max uses 4 unit cubes to make a 3D shape.

CHALLENGE

Draw as many different 3D shapes as you can with 4 unit cubes on the isometric grid below.

Reflect

Explain what is meant by volume. How do you measure volume?

Comparing volumes

1 Tick the shape in each set that has the greatest volume.

a)

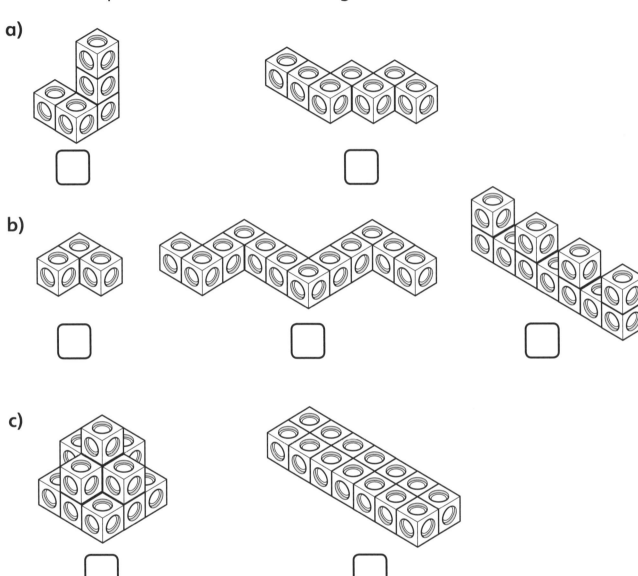

b)

c)

d) Did you need to count all the cubes in each shape?

Explain your answer.

_____

_____

_____

2 Sort these shapes. List them from greatest to least volume.

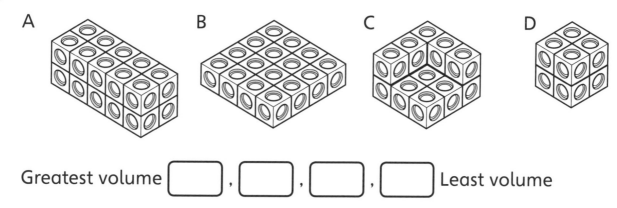

A   B   C   D

Greatest volume ⬚ , ⬚ , ⬚ , ⬚ Least volume

3 Match each shape to the correct person by writing their name under their shape.

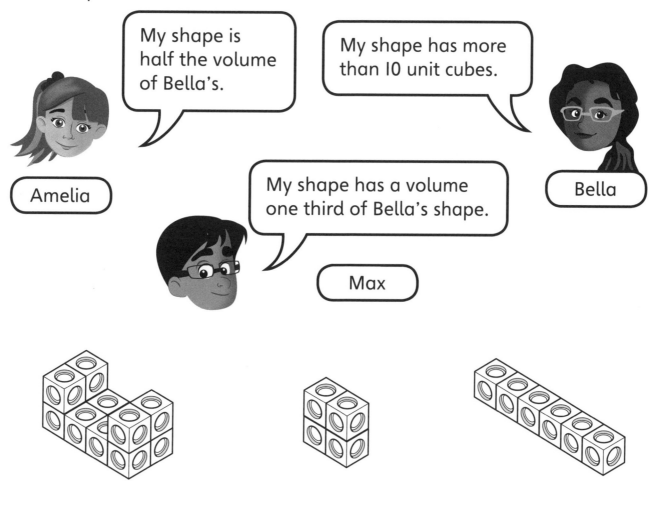

My shape is half the volume of Bella's.

My shape has more than 10 unit cubes.

Amelia

My shape has a volume one third of Bella's shape.

Bella

Max

_____   _____   _____

4. Add cubes to shape A so that it has the same volume as shape B.

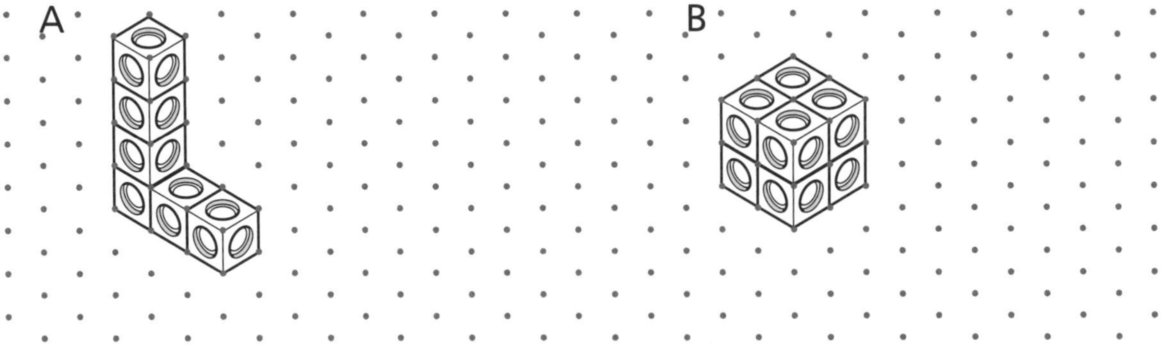

A

B

5. Aki makes a tower 15 cubes tall.

CHALLENGE

Emma makes a cuboid 4 cubes long, 2 cubes wide and 2 cubes high.

Predict who has made the shape with the greatest volume.

I predict that _____ has made the shape with the

greatest volume because _____ .

Now make each shape and check. Was your prediction correct?

_____

Reflect

Explain why two shapes that are made up of the same number of cubes can be different shapes but the same volume.

Estimating volume

1 Ambika estimates the volume of each 3D shape by making it with cubes.

a)

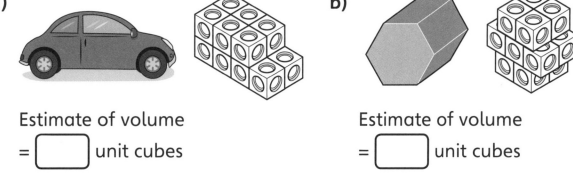

Estimate of volume

= ⬚ unit cubes

b)

Estimate of volume

= ⬚ unit cubes

2 Lexi builds some cubes to estimate the volume of her pencil.

Lexi says the volume of the pencil is 12 unit cubes.

How accurate do you think Lexi's estimate is? Explain your answer.

_____

_____

_____

3 Ebo has built this shape to estimate the volume of a 3D shape.

a) Tick the shape Ebo is estimating the volume of.

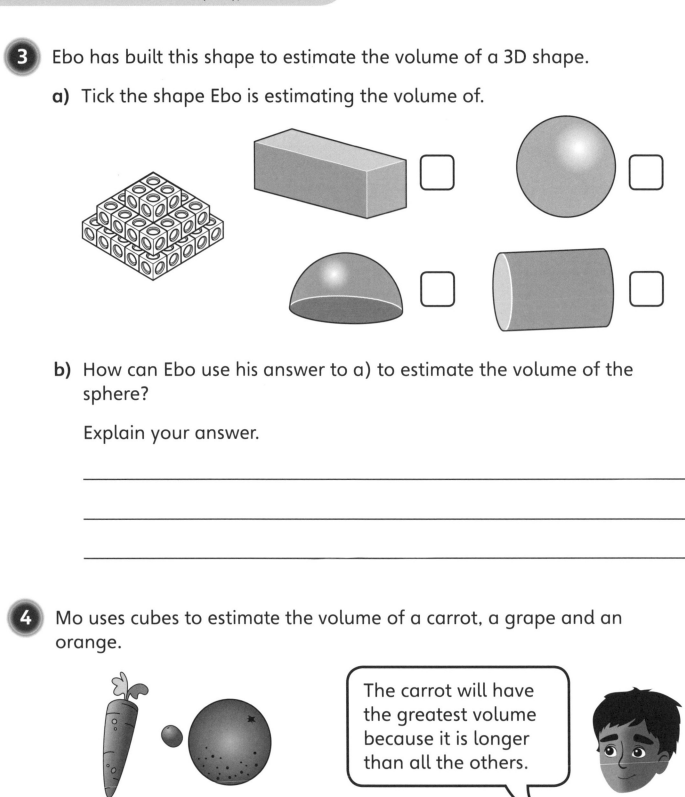

b) How can Ebo use his answer to a) to estimate the volume of the sphere?

Explain your answer.

_____

_____

_____

4 Mo uses cubes to estimate the volume of a carrot, a grape and an orange.

The carrot will have the greatest volume because it is longer than all the others.

Mo

Do you agree with Mo? Explain your answer.

_____

_____

5 Estimate the volume of the following items you might find in your school.

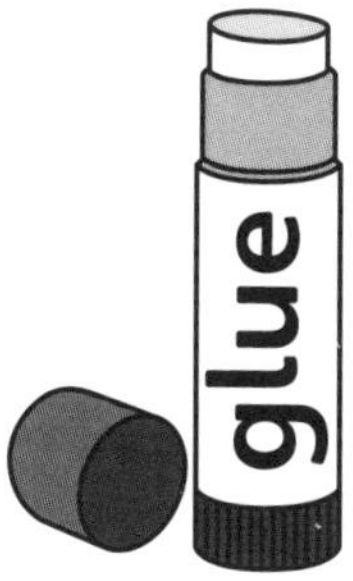

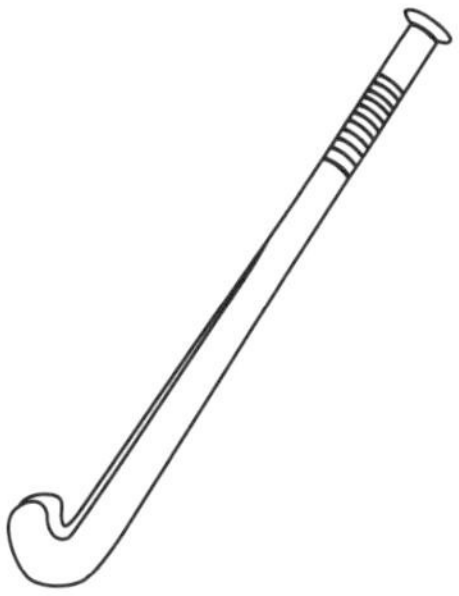

Estimate:

☐ unit cubes

Estimate:

☐ unit cubes

Estimate:

☐ unit cubes

CHALLENGE

6 Complete the table with objects you might find in the classroom or at home.

Volume of less than 10 unit cubes	Volume of between 10 and 100 unit cubes	Volume of between 100 and 1,000 unit cubes

Reflect

Explain how you could estimate the volume of your hand.

_____

_____

_____

Estimating capacity

1 Draw lines to match the best estimate of the capacity of each of these items.

| 10 ml | 750 ml | 7·5 l | 7 l | 70 l | 7,000 ml |

a)

b)

2 Circle the containers that can hold 2 litres of water or more.

1,000 ml

3 Put the following containers in order of capacity.

Start with the container that can hold the least.

A   B    C   D    E

Smallest capacity , , , , Greatest capacity

4 One litre of water has been poured into each vase. Estimate the capacity of each vase.

a)

[____] ml

b)

[____] ml

c)

[____] ml

5 Richard is pouring juice out of a big bottle into 200 ml glasses.

After pouring out two glasses, the bottle is $\frac{4}{5}$ full.

Estimate the capacity of one full bottle.

Explain your method.

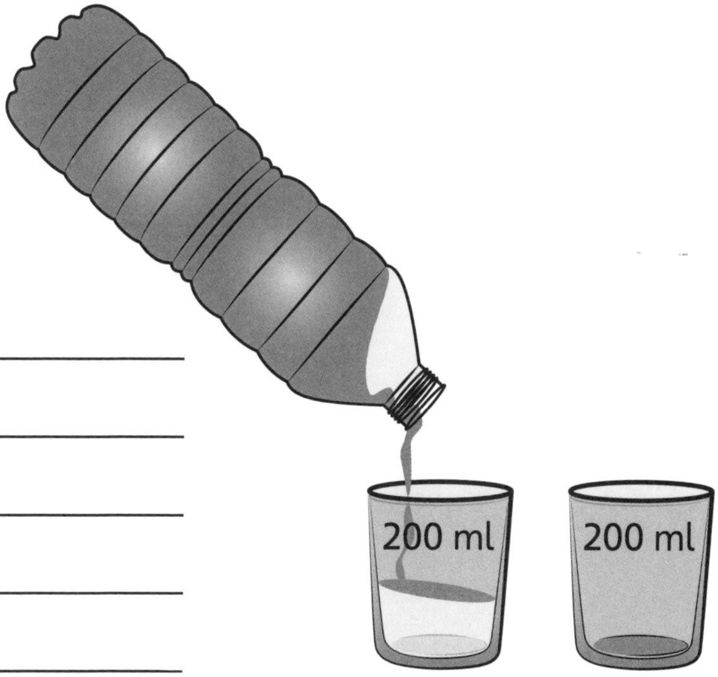

_____

_____

_____

_____

_____

200 ml   200 ml

The capacity of one full bottle is [____] ml.

6 There are two jugs.

Some water is poured out of jug A into jug B.

Jug A holds 500 ml of water.

Estimate how much water jug B holds.

Explain your method.

CHALLENGE

A   B

A   B

_____

_____

_____

Reflect

Explain the difference between volume and capacity.

_____

_____

_____

End of unit check

My journal

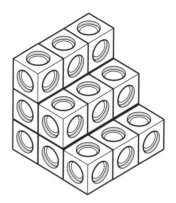

1 Explain two different ways to work out the volume of this shape.

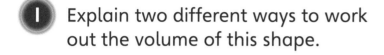

Power check

How do you feel about your work in this unit?

Power puzzle

How many footballs do you think could fit into your classroom?

Think about how you can make the most accurate estimate possible.

Explain your strategy clearly. Use both diagrams and words.

Use your workings to estimate the total number of footballs that could fit into the entire school.

My power points

Put a tick against the topics you have learnt about. Show how confident you are with each one by giving it a number on a scale of 1 to 3.

1 = not at all confident;
2 = getting there;
3 = very confident

Unit 12
I have learnt how to …

☐ Add and subtract decimals ☐

☐ Do decimal sequences ☐

☐ Solve problems using decimals ☐

☐ Multiply decimals by 10, 100 and 1,000 ☐

☐ Divide decimals by 10, 100 and 1,000 ☐

Unit 13
I have learnt how to …

☐ Measure angles in degrees ☐

☐ Use a protractor to measure angles ☐

☐ Draw lines and angles accurately ☐

☐ Calculate angles on a straight line ☐

☐ Calculate angles around a point ☐

☐ Calculate lengths and angles in shapes ☐

Unit 14

I have learnt how to ...

[ ] Recognise and draw parallel lines [ ]

[ ] Recognise and draw perpendicular lines [ ]

[ ] Deduce angles and properties of parallel and perpendicular lines [ ]

[ ] Reason about regular and irregular polygons [ ]

[ ] Understand the properties of 3D shapes [ ]

Unit 15

I have learnt how to ...

[ ] Draw the reflections of shapes using a grid [ ]

[ ] Use coordinates to draw reflections [ ]

[ ] Understand translations on a grid and use coordinates to describe them [ ]

Unit 16

I have learnt how to ...

[ ] Understand different metric units [ ]

[ ] Explain imperial units of length, mass and capacity [ ]

[ ] Convert units of time [ ]

[ ] Solve problems about timetables [ ]

Unit 17

I have learnt how to ...

☐ Understand different metric units

☐ Explain what volume is

☐ Compare different volumes

☐ Use cubes to estimate the volume and capacity of different solids or objects

☐
☐
☐
☐

You are doing great!

Notes